THE UNITED NATIONS AT WORK

Developing Land, Forests, Oceans,
. . . and People

THE UNITED NATIONS AT WORK

Developing Land, Forests, Oceans
. . . and People

BY

JOSEPH MARION JONES

Lecturer on International Development,
Fletcher School of Law and Diplomacy,
Tufts University

PERGAMON PRESS

OXFORD · LONDON · EDINBURGH · NEW YORK
PARIS · FRANKFURT

Pergamon Press Ltd., Headington Hill Hall, Oxford
4 & 5 Fitzroy Square, London W.1

Pergamon Press (Scotland) Ltd., 2 & 3 Teviot Place, Edinburgh 1

Pergamon Press Inc., 122 East 55th Street, New York 22, N.Y.

Pergamon Press GmbH, Kaiserstrasse 75, Frankfurt-am-Main

Federal Publications Ltd., Times House, River Valley Rd., Singapore

Samcax Book Services Ltd., Queensway, P.O. Box 2720, Nairobi, Kenya

Set in 10 on 12 pt. Plantin
and Printed in Great Britain by
Billing and Sons Ltd., Guildford and London

FOR LILIAN

FOREWORD

IN the prosperous industrialized nations, people who are daily admonished to cut their caloric intake may understandably find it difficult to realize that our planet remains basically a "hungry world". And with some countries actually burdened by vast agricultural surpluses, it is still harder to comprehend that in 20 years *or less* we could be faced with world-encircling famine.

Yet, even today, many hundreds of millions of people in the world's developing nations quite literally never have enough to eat. And, since the enervating effects of a bare subsistence diet are inevitably reflected in low levels of economic productivity and a high incidence of disease, such widespread chronic malnutrition tends to be self-perpetuating. Thus, even if the steep curve of world population growth should level off appreciably, tomorrow holds the very real prospect of starvation on an unthinkable scale—unless effective action is taken now to help the low-income nations greatly increase their food-producing capabilities.

Fortunately, with the help of modern science and technology, the seas, the lands, the rivers, and the waters under the earth can be made to increase their present yield of foodstuffs two, three, even ten times over. The United Nations and its related agencies are helping to direct and support history's first concerted international effort to achieve that goal—an effort which the author of this book describes as "the most hopeful enterprise of our time".

In these days, when economic assistance to the low-income nations is coming under increasingly critical (and sometimes hostile) scrutiny, it is imperative to increase understanding of the fact that poverty rather than politics lies at the root of so many recurrent disturbances which daily and dangerously disturb world peace. No less important is greater public awareness of what has already been accomplished in the war on global want through the efforts of the people of the developing countries supported by bilateral and multilateral economic assistance.

The creation of this increased awareness is a major purpose of the Freedom from Hunger Campaign now being waged on the initiative of the Food and Agriculture Organization's far-sighted Director-General, Dr. B. R. Sen.

I have known Dr. Joseph Marion Jones for many years, and have worked with him both during and since the Marshall Plan era. His extensive experience and the eye-witness investigations on which this book is based lend *The United Nations at Work* impressive authority and exciting human interest. Dr. Jones is no man to shy away from the controversial aspects of his chosen theme, nor does he gloss over the staggering problems confronting the Food and Agriculture Organization and other U.N. agencies in their efforts to help some 130 developing countries and territories speed social and economic progress. While *The United Nations at Work* highlights the drama of a billion and a half people struggling to improve their lot, it also provides a realistic appraisal of their progress, their prospects, and the impressive contributions made by the hardworking handful of international experts who have brought them aid under the U.N. banner.

PAUL G. HOFFMAN
Managing Director
United Nations Special Fund

AUTHOR'S NOTE

SHORTLY after arriving in Rome in October 1963 with nothing in mind but a long Mediterranean vacation, I ran into an old friend who, after greeting me warmly, declared that I had to stay and write a book. I had known Egon Glesinger since we had labored together on *Fortune* magazine in New York 20 years earlier, and now he was an Assistant Director General of the Food and Agriculture Organization of the United Nations.

"A book about what?"

"A book about FAO, of course."

I was not enthralled, but agreed to look through a stack of documents which he would assemble for me. Three weeks later I reported to him that FAO operations were so intertwined with other U.N. funds and agencies as to be inseparable from them. If a book was wanted, it should cover all U.N. activities as they relate to development of land, forests, and oceans.

There followed a proposition too attractive to refuse. I would write a book of whatever breadth and depth I desired. I would travel anywhere I wished seeking information. I would be provided with research and secretarial assistance. My expenses would, within limits, be covered. The book would be mine, without any attempt to influence what I should write and publish. These terms have been strictly honored.

After two months of preparatory study and interviews, during which I also observed a biennial FAO Conference in session in Rome, I set out upon a 75-day trip which took me to Egypt, Thailand, Chile, Senegal, and Morocco. And then I returned to Rome where, fed by a stream of U.N. documents, I wrote this book.

It is unusual for an outsider to be invited in such manner into the U.N. family circle and given *carte blanche* to observe and report whatever he sees. For that opportunity I am grateful to Dr. B. R. Sen, Director General, and Dr. Egon Glesinger, Assistant Director

General, of the Food and Agriculture Organization of the United Nations, and also to Mr. Paul G. Hoffman, Managing Director of the U.N. Special Fund, to Mr. David Owen, Executive Chairman of the U.N. Technical Assistance Board, to Mr. A. H. Boerma, Executive Director of the World Food Program, and to Mr. Charles H. Weitz, Coordinator of the Freedom from Hunger Campaign. They opened the doors. But my thanks go equally to a host of FAO officers, technical experts, and staff members in Rome and in the field, to the U.N. Resident Representatives and UNICEF directors in the countries where I traveled, and to dozens of the real heroes of international development—the men and women who are carrying on development projects in the field. They showed me paths, eased my way, and I am grateful.

No less am I indebted to government officials in the countries where I sought information. Not only were they cordial but also helpful in generous measure. Hassan Abdallah, Director of Foreign Relations in the Ministry of Agriculture in Cairo, an authority on FAO aid to agriculture, went so far beyond duty and normal courtesy that I must give him a special salute.

Likewise deserving of special recognition were the help, advice, and encouragement given to me by Mr. Clinton Rehling, Assistant to the Managing Director of the U.N. Special Fund.

I do not think I could have accomplished my purpose without the help of Miss Winifred Thompson, who steered me through mountains of documents and directed me to the right people for facts and figures, or without the cheerful competence of Miss Rosemary Cooper. To them my enduring gratitude.

A writer's job is to simplify and clarify a subject, but in writing about international development he tends, in spite of conscious resistance, to be infected by the abominable jargon of the trade. My severest critic was my wife, Lilian Grosvenor Jones, whose sensitivity to "officialese" is acute. I will not say that "without her comfort and help . . . ", because she often made me uncomfortable. But she did a great deal to make my manuscript more readable and I am grateful to her.

Washington, D.C., 17 *March* 1965

CONTENTS

LIST OF ABBREVIATIONS

ACC	Administrative Committee on Co-ordination (of the United Nations)
AID	U.S. Agency for International Development
CIDA	Inter-American Committee for Agricultural Development
DERRO	Développement Economique de la Région du Rif Occidentale — Economic Development of the Western Rif Region (Morocco)
ECA	Economic Commission for Africa (U.N.)
ECLA	Economic Commission for Latin America (U.N.)
ECOSOC	Economic and Social Council (U.N.)
EPTA	Expanded Program of Technical Assistance
FAO	Food and Agriculture Organization of the United Nations
IAEA	International Atomic Energy Agency (U.S.)
IBRD	International Bank for Reconstruction and Development (U.N.)
ICAO	International Civil Aviation Organization (U.N.)
IDA	International Development Association (U.N.)
IDB	Inter-American Development Bank
IIAS	Inter-American Institute of Agricultural Sciences
IFC	International Finance Corporation (U.N.)
ILO	International Labour Organization (U.N.)
IMF	International Monetary Fund (U.N.)
IMCO	Inter-governmental Maritime Consultative Organization (U.N.)
ITU	International Telecommunication Union (U.N.)
OAS	Organization of American States
OCA	Office de Commercialisation Agricole (Senegal)
OMNR	Office Nationale de Modernisation Rurale (Morocco)
PRAM	Project for the Modernization of Agriculture in Morocco

SDAI	Société de Développement Agricole et Industriel (Senegal)
SEDAC	Société du Développement de l'Arachide et de Céréale (Senegal)
SOSEPA	Société Sénégalaise de Produits Alimentaires (Senegal)
U.N.	United Nations
UNSF	U.N. Special Fund
UNICEF	U.N. Children's Fund
UNESCO	U.N. Educational Scientific and Cultural Organization
UPU	Universal Postal Union
UNRRA	U.N. Relief and Rehabilitation Administration
WHO	World Health Organization
WFP	World Food Program
WMO	World Meteorological Organization

PART I

Land, Forests, Oceans . . . and People

CHAPTER I

THE MOST
HOPEFUL ENTERPRISE OF OUR TIME

THE effort that has been undertaken in our generation to extend to all men and all countries the knowledge and capital needed to put the earth's lands, forests, and oceans to more productive use is something new under the sun, and yet after 20 years it is so vast and complex as to defy statement or comprehension. It is the most hopeful enterprise of our time. Already it is bringing about an unfolding in human thought and a stimulation of activity that can be compared in quality and impact only to the Renaissance of the fifteenth century and the Industrial Revolution of the eighteenth. And our new age has only just begun.

This unfolding is the logical consequence of historical trends over centuries, but historical trends were obliged in a single generation to lacerate the human race with two terrible, devastating world wars, a massive world depression, and a threat of total atomization to teach their lesson. It was only during the suffering of World War II that the spiritual and intellectual bases of the great enterprise with which we are here concerned were laid. Afterwards, the disintegration of the world's colonial empires and the emergence of dozens of weak and inexperienced national states made it even more obvious that there must be shared use of capital, knowledge and skills if there were to be a semblance of international order or prosperity.

In most of the countries of the world people are poor chiefly because they do not have the knowledge, or the skill, or the organization to be otherwise. Anybody can scratch the earth, plant some left-over seed from the last crop (unless it has spoiled or been eaten) and leave the rest to the vagaries of sun and rain. Anybody can cut a tree or saw or hack out a piece of lumber, or go out in a primitive dugout and catch a few fish, or herd some skinny cattle or sheep or goats in a sparse pasture. And this is just what most of the people in poor countries do. This is also why they are desperately poor and hungry.

But travel today to the capital of any one of a hundred of the less-developed countries of the world, keep your eyes and ears open, and you cannot fail to be impressed with the determination of the government, and of the opposition if there is one, to force the pace of modernization. You have already probably arrived late because the earlier plane was filled with officials and development experts. Your hotel is likely to be pack-jammed because of some development conference. The people at the next table in the restaurant are likely to be talking about some aspect of development. The newspapers each day are full of the subject. The offices, the halls, the corridors of the government ministries buzz with conversations and plans and projects and itineraries undreamed of 20 years ago. The busiest offices in town are likely to be those of the planning board, the development corporation, the development bank.

"Competitive benevolence" in foreign aid by the United States, the U.S.S.R., and other countries is responsible for many of the more spectacular and publicized features of this activity. And aside from the cold war a great deal of other assistance flowing across national boundaries today arises from considerations of national prestige and international politics. But it is a superficial view that these are the only or most fundamental impulses in the great enterprise. That international rivals nowadays choose development assistance as an implement to gain political advantage is a sign that new thoughts and aspirations have indeed acquired influence in the world.

Government and politics in a hundred countries of the world are overwhelmingly preoccupied with development, for it is no longer safe politically, or physically either for that matter, not to be. Time was when governments in these countries could survive merely by placating the army and a few leading citizens in the big cities and by policing the crowded city slums, but no longer. Now they have to cope with the students, with small but growing groups of educated, critical professionals, with agitation to bring about change by violent means, and more importantly with the millions of illiterate and poverty-ridden masses of people up country who are now not far from a transistor radio and perhaps a new road to the capital. The inescapable facts of modern life — everywhere — force governments to try to extend more of the opportunities for a decent life to more people.

Directly or indirectly stimulating this development, imparting to it their knowledge and skills, often financing part of it, involved right up to the hilt in it, is the legion of foreign experts recruited and furnished by the United Nations or other international organizations, by other governments, and by foreign private agencies. Nor are these experts operating alone. They are backed up by organizations and governments which have vast stores of accumulated knowledge and which stand ready within the limits of their budgets to respond still further to calls for help. It would be difficult to overestimate the importance of the role of the foreign experts and their home organizations in the development effort of a poor country. To appreciate it one must try to imagine the crushing loneliness and frustration that would engulf a country's leaders if, without enough trained people or institutions to train them, or enough research laboratories, or knowledge of their resources and how to exploit them, they were obliged to contemplate a national development program without help from the outside. Under those circumstances they would not undertake much of a program, for improvement or progress in any line necessarily begins with a conviction that something can be done.

But today they are not alone. The help is there — certainly not enough of it, but enough to inspire hope, confidence, intense activity, and without any question some progress.

The unobtrusive pale blue and white flags you see in the capital city mark the local offices of the agencies and organs of the U.N. family whose representatives are there to help in the transfer of capital and knowledge and skills. The big building across the square houses the U.S. aid mission, and scattered about the city may be the aid missions of the U.S.S.R., of Great Britain, of France, or of a dozen other countries, or the local offices of foreign private foundations, or of large foreign Protestant, Catholic, or Jewish organizations, or of private foreign corporations or consulting firms — all engaged in helping bring about the great transfer. This new government building on your right is to house the new nutrition institute, that one to train medical technicians, and those two down the street house fisheries and forestry institutes, all organized with U.N. help and partially staffed for a limited number of years by U.N. experts. Whatever the results thus far, the activity is extensive and impressive. There is no doubt that it is laying the scientific, technological and social bases of modern life in countries where hitherto they have been largely absent.

Travel about the country and you cannot go far without seeing other evidence of the transfer. The main road by which you travel may very well have been built with American aid, and the big dam you visit and the power lines extending across country from it with loans from the World Bank. Go deeper into the farmlands or the bush or the forests or the desert fringe, and the jeeps and trucks you see bouncing along on rudimentary roads are likely to contain a foreign soil surveyor or doctor or teacher or nutritionist or meteorologist, or forester or hydrologist or one of a hundred different kinds of technical experts, each accompanied by his local "counterpart". The hillside you see there is covered by demonstration "banquettes", cheaper than terraces for controlling erosion and directing rain water where it is best stored and used, the project advised by a U.N. expert. In that luxuriant field a fertilizer demonstration project is under way; the relatively barren field next to it has had no fertilizer. The line of newly afforested hills in the distance was designed as a windbreak. In the school you are passing nutritional feeding, training and demonstration are being carried on, and in the next a similar project in new educational techniques. And so on, in great variety.

Equally important are the things that are going on in the country that have little or no visible impact — you just have to discover them: the new technical training courses in the local university; the travels of technicians and administrators to hundreds of international meetings, seminars, and training courses; the work going on in the laboratories to adapt more productive strains of rice or wheat, to breed more productive livestock, to protect both plants and animals from the pests and diseases to which they are prey. Often with the advice of foreign experts, the planning board is in daily session struggling with priorities in the use of local resources and foreign aid. New institutions established with the help of foreign aid and advised by foreign experts are grappling with the problems of credit to farmers and small industries. And in the government departments young administrators and technicians who studied abroad on fellowships provided by foreign or international agencies, or who attended a training session abroad, or who were inspired and trained at home by the foreign expert with whom he was assigned to work for a period, are carrying on brilliant and effective work. This activity is not photogenic as yet; it probably has not made a dramatic impact on statistics. It is slow, patient, slogging work. But it is the most promising work in the world.

Science and technology and administration are not static, a neatly circumscribed body of accumulated knowledge to be transferred in a package. They are changing at a dizzy pace, and advancing knowledge must be constantly sought and adapted to the special soils and climates and people and traditions that exist in any particular country. Foreign experts are enormously helpful as they study and advise on specific problems and projects and policies. However, they are even more effective as they influence the building and operation of local training and research institutions whose chief products are trained people in touch with the advancing world knowledge of their profession, able to draw from it and adapt to it local conditions. But this is only the beginning. The most staggering problem in most of the underdeveloped countries is how to extend even the simpler, proven methods from the institutions of the capital to scattered, illiterate, tradition-steeped people living as did their forebears hundreds of years ago.

"Trained people to do a job, trained people to train others, that's what I need" — this is the impassioned declaration of the modern administrator in any less developed country. "If I were to be given tomorrow the choice between 200 trained men and 200 million dollars, I'd choose the men," said to me a young Senegalese administrator, his eyes blazing.

Thus do the big words — the great transfer of knowledge, science and technology — boil down in essence to building institutions and influencing and training people who will in turn acquire and adapt knowledge and train other people who will in due course educate other millions of people.

Capital transfer through grant or loan or direct investment for building dams and factories and ports and railways is necessary to development. But the ability of a country to attract and use capital, public or private, depends either upon pre-existing knowledge, technical plans, and technical capacity, or upon the successful training-on-the-job of administrators and technicians, or upon turning the entire job over to foreigners, a circumstance growing rarer. In general, capital transfer and knowledge transfer need each other and must proceed together. Capital investment alone cannot do the development job, especially in that majority of the countries of the world which is overwhelmingly agricultural.

The large and growing gap between average incomes in the more advanced countries of the world and those in the poorer countries is a matter of grave international concern. And experience teaches that there can be no narrowing of the income gap except with a prior or at least accompanying narrowing of the knowledge gap. Capital breeds capital. But likewise knowledge begets knowledge and training begets training. The most hopeful enterprise of our time is stepping up a transfer of capital, knowledge and training so that in the less developed countries they may breed there at an accelerating rate and lay the basis for sound economic and social progress.

CHAPTER 2

THE TRANSFER OF KNOWLEDGE

No matter how poor a country might be, it has land and people, and more than likely it has forests, rivers and lakes, and access to the resources of the oceans. These are elementary resources upon which man is ultimately dependent for his basic needs: food, clothing, and shelter. We are concerned here with what the U.N. family of organizations is doing to help extend the benefits of modern science to the production, processing, storage, marketing, and consumption of food, fish, fibers, and wood in the underdeveloped countries of the world. As all might agree, this is a big part of the development job. Food alone is the biggest business in the world. Every person on earth must eat it and does eat it, several times a day if he can. Most of the people in the underdeveloped countries either grow food, or raise it, or catch it in river or ocean, or transport it, or store it, or process it, or sell it. In spite of this most of them cannot grow enough food or afford to buy enough of it to quell their hunger and keep them healthy and vigorous. The reason is that they carry on agriculture, fishing, and forestry largely without benefit of modern science, method, or organization. The result is low yields, poverty, and hunger.

The United Nations is deeply committed to the task of extending knowledge, capital, and organization to the agriculture, forestry, and fisheries of underdeveloped countries. The chief agencies and organs engaged in this work are the Food and Agriculture Organization of the United Nations (FAO), the U.N. Expanded Program of Technical Assistance (EPTA), the U.N. Special Fund, the U.N. Children's Fund (UNICEF), the World Food Program (WFP), the World Bank, and the International Development Association (IDA). However, the chief agent of the United Nations in so far as food, agriculture, forestry, and fisheries are concerned, and the only agency occupied exclusively with these, is the U.N. Food and Agriculture Organization (FAO).

The U.N. family does not, of course, have any monopoly on the extension of knowledge and capital for the development of agriculture, forestry, and fisheries. Far from it. Many individual countries are engaged bilaterally in the same enterprise, some of them heavily. Likewise regional international organizations, private foundations, and corporations are busy.

The first thing that hits you when you look behind the façade of agriculture, forestry, and fisheries is their staggering complexity. Development means applying better methods to bring about higher yields and incomes. But what an endless nightmare of scientific and technical knowledge is concealed behind those mild words "better methods"! Most of us non-farmers have heard vaguely of fertilizers, crop rotation, hybrid corn, the boll weevil and wheat rust, irrigation, afforestation, the tsetse fly, and perhaps even contour plowing. But surely not even a farmer or a trained agriculturist knows much about many of the hundreds of scientific and technical specialties needed to increase the yields of the world's soils, paddies, pastures, forests and oceans, in storing, transporting, processing and marketing them, and in improving nutrition and incomes.

Six food grains feed most of the world — rice, wheat, corn (maize), barley, millet, and sorghum — and of these rice feeds the most. Now, rice would seem to be such a simple plant. In fact, it is one of the most sensitive and complex, requiring the utmost application of science for high yields. There are 1366 major varieties of rice catalogued by FAO and thousands of lesser ones, each responding differently to varying combinations of soils, waters, temperatures, fertilizers, and day-lengths (in the Far East 1 minute's difference in day-length may mean as much as 3 days' difference in rice maturity). Each also varies in resistance to diseases and in milling quality. Substitute a higher for a lower yield variety in any particular environment, or add a fertilizer, and you probably increase susceptibility to rice *blast* or some other rice disease. Once the rice is harvested, large portions of it are likely to be destroyed by rats and insects in farm storage or lost in the milling process — unless adequate storage facilities are built and proper milling methods used. No, rice growing is not simple. Thailand, although the world's biggest rice exporting country, has one of the lowest rice yields per acre in the world. Japan has one of the highest because it has used modern science and technology effectively in rice growing.

Listed in FAO catalogues are no less than 2000 varieties (genetic stocks) of wheat, some 3000 of maize, and about 250 of barley — each with yields varying, as do those of rice, according to local environment. In addition, all vary in resistance to their inevitable diseases, all are attacked in the field by insects of various kinds, in storage by rodents and other pests, and in milling by equally destructive ignorance, tradition and carelessness. In addition to grains, there are many thousands of different fruits, roots, vegetables, seeds, pulses, nuts, spices, and fibers grown in the world, and of them this may be said without contradiction: there is not one of them that cannot be produced in far greater quantity or better quality per unit of land or labor if enough attention with modern methods is paid to breeding, or fertilizing, or watering, or protection against the myriad diseases and pests that attack them.

The production and protection (against disease and pests) of improved livestock and poultry raise problems no less complex than those relating to plants. Underdeveloped livestock — beef cattle, dairy cattle, sheep and goats, pigs — are typical in an underdeveloped country. Skinny, runty, impoverished, they roam impoverished pastures, herded carefully by children and men as though they were of enormous value, whereas in fact their yield in either meat, milk or wool is extremely low. In some countries this is due partly to religious taboo, as in India, or to social custom and tradition, as in Nigeria and in many countries of Africa, where herds and flocks are traditional status symbols from whose number the owner draws social and political satisfaction in preference to nutrition or income. But chiefly the low yield is due simply to habit and ignorance and lack of either inspiration or help to make any change.

The beginning of improvement, if there is anybody to show the way, is the introduction of new strains of livestock and their crossing with hardy native strains. Another step is the enrichment of pastures, better range management, the growing of fodder crops, and the production of improved livestock feeds generally. Then comes commercialization of the market, building facilities for transporting, handling and processing meat — all involving highly technical problems.

Breeding and feeding improved livestock and poultry are simple compared with protecting them from virulent, contagious diseases and parasites which frequently devastate them in Asia, Africa and Latin America and which from time to time threaten to sweep through Europe. Rinderpest, unless controlled, wipes out cattle in whole regions. Foot-and-mouth disease, equally contagious, causes weight loss, reduction in milk yields, loss of calves and sterility in breeding stock, and absenteeism and apathy on the part of draft animals. Cows also get pleuro-pneumonia and tuberculosis and a variety of other dread diseases. And in four million square miles of Africa the tsetse fly, carrying a disease which boasts the name of trypanosomiasis, kills livestock on such a scale as to make them exceedingly scarce. Hogs succumb to African fever or cholera. Sheep and goats have a variety of contagious pox to draw upon. Horses are doomed with a rapidly spreading African sickness. And poultry die by the millions from Newcastle disease. This is only a beginning roster, but we might as well leave it here. These diseases can be prevented or controlled, but it takes elaborate scientific research, large-scale programs of vaccination or immunization or slaughtering, and excellent, frequently international, organization and administration.*

Animal diseases and migratory pests such as locusts are of far more than local interest for they know no national boundaries and do not even know the difference between an underdeveloped country and a developed one. For example, within the last 5 years African horse-sickness appeared suddenly in the Middle East and in an area extending from Turkey to India killed 200,000 to 300,000

---

* Under the vigorous direction since 1951 of a highly knowledgeable Australian, K. V. L. Kestenen, FAO's work in this field has rendered untold service to our generation.

horses and mules before being brought under control with FAO help; an especially virulent African foot-and-mouth disease appeared in the Middle East from Africa and spread all over from European Turkey to Pakistan; and an African type swine-fever, unfamiliar in Europe, a type for which no vaccine had been developed, appeared in Spain and Portugal, and more recently in France. But for FAO action, these epidemics might have extended through Europe.

Continuing with agriculture's complexities, we have to consider the habits and caprices of rainfall and water supply, for the growing of food everywhere is vitally concerned with enough water, too much water or too little, flood or drought. The body of knowledge that has been built up over thousands of years for coping with the vagaries of nature regarding rainfall and water supply is immense, but highly technical, frequently expensive, unevenly known and applied, and by no means complete. Floods can be countered with dams, reservoirs, and controlled irrigation, or prevented by proper attention to forests. Torrential rains which wash out crops and cause erosion can often be handled with proper crop or ground cover, plowing practices, water impoundment for use in periods of no rain, and by afforestation. Swamps can often be reclaimed by means of proper dikes and drainage, and deserts by irrigation. Semi-arid areas can frequently be made more productive through exploring for ground water and digging shallow wells, through improved dry-farming practices, and range management.

There is much that can be done if a country knows how to do it and has the money and organization to do it. But it has to know what it is doing, and it needs all the technical help and advice it can get. Irrigation alone is far more complicated than it would seem. A vast acreage in Pakistan irrigated for decades is now saline and relatively barren because of insufficient attention to drainage. The entire Nile Valley cultivated for thousands of years with the help of flood waters from the Nile is in danger of becoming waterlogged and saline, with a consequent reduction in yields, now that dams, reservoirs, river flow control, and irrigation throughout the year make possible two or three crops a year in response to the needs of a fast growing population on limited arable land. These conditions can be corrected through applied science and technology, experimentation, and large expenditures, and the United Nations is helping in both Pakistan and Egypt.

Fish is more than just another food. It is a food especially rich in the protein which is sadly deficient in the diets of most of the people in the world. Fish and other forms of edible marine life are available in enormous supply, if you know how to catch them, in the oceans which wash the coasts of all but a few countries of the world, and also in rivers and lakes. However, in most of those countries the catching of fish is still largely an individualistic hit-and-miss affair, marketing is rudimentary and wasteful, and consumption is more or less limited to coastal areas of countries while inland people suffer from hunger and malnutrition. The governments of underdeveloped countries are therefore eager to stimulate fish catching, marketing, processing, local consumption, and perhaps exportation. And it is important to the world that in the process fish resources be conserved and cultivated.

All of this is not as easy as it sounds. It depends upon surveys of resources, compilation of statistics, elaborate marine biology research, more efficient fishing boats and equipment for detecting, catching, landing, processing (freezing, drying, smoking, canning, curing, production of fish meal), training of fishermen and fisheries scientists, development of markets, and other specialties that would require two or three pages to list. It takes a lot of knowledge and effort these days for a country to undergird a profitable fishing enterprise and the industry and trade based upon it, but the increased nutrition, employment, living standards and national income accruing from the effort may be very high indeed.

Forestry is not farming and forest products are not food, but they affect land-use, and vitally influence farming, farm income, and national income from the land. In most countries of the world forests have been cleared, burned, or ruthlessly and wastefully exploited. In only a few countries, and even there only in the last few years, have they been systematically managed and protected and developed as a valuable national resource. It has only been in the last 30 or 40 years that the relation between forests and protection of the farmer's land-capital (or to put it another way, the relation between deforestation, dustbowls, floods, and erosion) has achieved any very wide recognition. Only in the last 10 years has it been realized widely that scientific forest management and exploitation in dozens of less developed countries and the encouragement there of forest industries — wood pulp, paper, plywood, and fiber boards — can make a powerful contribution to national wealth. But the technical specialties required for modern forestry are so numerous as to defy brief description. They extend all the way from resource surveys, national forest policy planning, the genetics of quick-growing species, and the fight against tree diseases, to the selection and care of tools. Speaking of the care of tools, in some of the small sawmills of southern Chile from 25 to 40 per cent of the product is lost simply because the operators do not know how to take care of their saws. Dozens of them are now going to a "saw doctor" school in Concepcion, learning how from a cheerful French-Canadian sent by FAO and paid by EPTA.

A prosperous agriculture, a well-fed people, a developing nation depends increasingly upon food technology, which is a large field of knowledge concerned with the processing and packaging of food and the marketing of the finished product. Processing means grinding, mixing, converting, preserving, canning, freezing, curing, drying or smoking, and these are complicated specialties. Packaging is an art, and marketing requires skill, knowledge, and organization.

Nutrition is one of the most important and frustrating sciences in the world. It is also one of the most fruitful. A relatively new field, not nearly enough is known about it and even nutrition standards and statistics are in dispute. Two things, however, are clear. One is that most of the people in the world do not get enough proteins to keep them in health or full vigor, and some, especially infants and children, not enough to ward off diseases stemming directly from malnutrition. The other is that enough *is* known about nutrition to keep most people well nourished if ways could be found to persuade or enable, say, a billion and a half people to grow or buy, and eat, the right kinds of foods. An attack on malnutrition means an attack upon ignorance, poverty, habit, tradition, and remoteness, as well as on the mountainous technical, organizational, and administrative difficulties involved in producing and distributing the proper foods. But the attack must be made and is being made. United Nations agencies are playing key roles.

Of the essence of the problem of nutrition and to a large degree identical with it, even though larger in scope, is the problem of extension: how to extend even the knowledge and improved methods which may be known to a few people in the research laboratories, universities, or government offices of a country's capital to the millions of people scattered on the land and in the villages. Knowledge is one thing; getting it diffused, accepted, and applied in low income countries with high illiteracy and poor communications is quite another. Extension services have worked miracles in the agriculture of the United States and a number of other advanced countries and enough is known about organizing and administering national extension services to make it a professional specialty in itself. The methods of extension include demonstration, community organization, the distribution of suitable literature, and radio broadcasts. But what an appalling, endless job lies behind these words! Governments desperately need help and they seek it, but the obstacles to significant progress are gigantic.

Statistics are a tool essential to governments trying to improve their agriculture, forests, and fisheries. FAO plays the central role in collecting agricultural, forestry, and fishery statistics from the countries of the world and in analyzing, publishing, and disseminating them. But statistics are no more useful than their accuracy, and FAO has therefore not only waged a continuous battle with national governments for more accurate statistics collected by improved methods, but also provides expert advice and on-the-spot expert assistance to governments seeking to sharpen their statistical tools. This is a highly complex business, requiring technical knowledge and informed judgement of a high order, for there are sampling techniques being perfected today which, aided by new machines for data processing, are much cheaper, more accurate, and speedier than old-fashioned enumeration.

There are many countries in Latin America, Asia, and Africa

where, no matter whatever else is done, agriculture will not thrive without thoroughgoing land reform and agricultural credit. To work assiduously a farmer must have incentive and that incentive must be either ownership of his own land or an adequate share of what he produces from his labor. And to improve his methods he must have credit on reasonable terms. Land reform is a national, political act, but a vast amount of experience and knowledge has been accumulated on how to draft laws and apply them in the national interest. The efficient organization and operation of agricultural credit institutions also requires knowledge and experience. U.N. agencies provide technical help and advice to governments in both these fields. Moreover, they provide expert help in organizing and managing farmers' cooperatives and building and operating rural community centers.

The United Nations also renders expert help and advice to governments in *planning* the development of their agriculture, forests, and fisheries, so as to make the most effective use of a limited supply of money and trained men. Increasingly it has come to be realized that a spotty, project-by-project approach is neither the fastest nor the most economical way to progress, but that national development planning is necessary, and that agriculture, forestry, and fishery development must be planned as a vital sector of an overall development plan. But planning depends on knowledge and skills and experience in short supply in the countries most in need of it. FAO therefore provides agricultural planning experts, when governments ask for them, and through regional conferences, seminars and training centers it spreads the attitudes and methods of planning. Soil surveys (which soils are suitable for growing what, where) and forest resource surveys are the foundations for national land use plans, and these surveys must be made by experts commanding specialized knowledge and equipment.

Any country's agriculture, forests, and fisheries are only a part, though in most less developed countries an overwhelming part, of its national economy which is governed by national laws and policies regarding taxation, credit, land tenure, imports and exports, and priorities in the use of national revenue and foreign aid. And a country's national economy is a part of the world economy, affected vitally by world markets for raw materials, by world prices (prices paid for raw materials which the less developed countries export, prices of industrial products which they must import, and the disparity between the two), and by world restrictions on imports. Science and technology without end can never help a country build or maintain a prosperous agriculture unless essential elements of its national economy are geared for it and unless the world economy is operating well and fairly. The United Nations, therefore, is necessarily concerned with the functioning of national economies and of the world economy as they affect food and agriculture. FAO and the other members of the U.N. family thus give advice and help to national governments, and ceaselessly they study the world economy and raise their voices in international councils on behalf of what they consider wise and just policies affecting food and agriculture.

We who live in more advanced countries, plagued more by surplus production from land and sea than by scarcity, tend to regard productive agriculture, forestry, and fisheries as rather simple and to take for granted the complex science, know-how, and organization upon which they are based. And yet, the knowledge foundation of our high productivity was built slowly and painfully over many generations, and today it depends upon a gigantic web of public and private institutions constantly at work, largely unseen. But a body of knowledge and a web of services, however, are only the beginning. The individual farmer, forester, and fisherman must somehow acquire the necessary knowledge and make its daily use part of his habit. There, in the human equation, is the stubbornest part of the problem.

The task of transferring to two-thirds of the world's people the knowledge, institutions and services for making land, forests, and oceans more productive is the biggest job ever consciously undertaken by man. But the harsh realities of the new world in which we live, outlined in the next chapter, compel him to make the effort.

CHAPTER 3

HARSH REALITIES OF OUR NEW WORLD

SIXTY new sovereign and independent nations whose territories were formerly ruled by European colonial powers have come into existence in the last 25 years, ranging in size from India with a present population of nearly 500 million to Malta with 315,000.

The rate of world population growth has increased from 1 per cent to 2 per cent annually in our generation. In most of the under-developed countries the rates of population increase are higher than the world average — from 2 to $3\frac{1}{2}$ per cent.

Twenty-five years ago the time required to travel from any world capital to the antipodes was from 1 to 3 months. Now, jet planes make it in 24 hours. In the poorest of countries today, the capital or the leading seaport or commercial center may be reached from the hinterland by road or air in minutes or hours, instead of days or weeks. The whole world, including remote, primitive peoples living in the bush, can today be reached almost instantaneously by radio.

Until the last 20 years, poverty, ignorance, hunger, servitude, and early death were unquestioned as being the inevitable lot of most of the people on earth. Today, the inevitability of these conditions is sharply questioned by people everywhere. First, alien rule was challenged and political independence achieved. And this has swelled an unprecedented tide of rising expectations for better conditions of life, a tide which sweeps onward and outward.

A quarter of a century ago concepts of social justice and social welfare as responsibilities of government had reached their first flower only in the most advanced countries of the West, and even there they were sharply challenged. Today they are well established not only there but everywhere. Twenty-five years ago the idea that the richer and more fortunate nations should help the poorer, not only as a matter of self-interest but also of morality, scarcely existed except in religious mission circles. Today, it is growing so rapidly in minds and hearts that it must be considered as a major political fact of life.

In 1939 the poorer countries of the world had little leverage on the rich who were fighting among themselves for world power. They were merely pawns who would fall to the winner. Today, the ability of the two super-powers, the United States and the Soviet Union, to destroy each other, and the world into the bargain, is in stalemate, and new patterns of power contest have emerged. Most countries, including the super-powers, now seek to extend their influence by means short of war. This has endowed the poorer and weaker countries with a leverage on the richer and stronger of a kind they have never before enjoyed. Whatever may be their national ambitions, they can now apply for help, or threaten to apply, to the United States, or to the Soviet Union, or to Mainland China, or to Nasser, or to Tito, or to Israel, or to any number of other countries which seek to extend their influence. And there is no country that can today expect to maintain or extend its influence without responding in some degree to the calls of other countries for help. This new international pattern of power contest on the part of the stronger countries and leverage on the part of the weaker is something new under the sun, and one of the most remarkable developments of our generation. It has many unpleasant aspects, and many constructive ones. In any case, it is preferable to war.

However, the underprivileged countries today have an alternative to help from individual countries and the risk of getting drawn into their power struggles. They can seek help from the United Nations and its family of organizations. This they increasingly prefer to do if the help is available there.

These, then, are some of the new realities of the world in which we live. As expressed they are not necessarily harsh. In fact, a number of them are benign and hopeful. But some of them have aspects and implications, to be considered now, that are harsh in the extreme.

One's spirits may or may not be lifted by the thought of vanished empires and the advent of sixty new sovereign states, but they are bound to plummet when one thinks about the problems raised by their independence. Without exception, the new countries are "underdeveloped" and have these conditions in common:

Low *per capita* income — an average of about $100 a year in Asia, Africa, and Latin America.

Low rates of savings and investment.

High proportion of the labor force engaged in agriculture, low industrial output in relation to population.

Widespread hunger and malnutrition.

High illiteracy; low educational level.

High birth rates, rapid population growth; high percentage of dependent children.

Poor roads, transport, and communications; inadequate supplies of power and light.

High incidence of disease, poor health, especially maternal and child health; few hospitals and other medical services.

Colonial administrations differed greatly in their concern for these problems, and it would in any case be unfair to judge their performance by the ethical and social expectations of today. By and large, their chief functions were to defend the territories from outside aggression, maintain internal order, and within the limits of local revenues to create conditions as favorable as possible for private investment and foreign trade. These major responsibilities required a certain amount of attention to seaports and waterways, major road arteries, railroads and telegraphs, minimum government services and even, spottily, to health, education, and social welfare. The standards and goals of the services rendered by even the most enlightened colonial administrations, however, were far below those expected today by the newly independent peoples. They scarcely touched, or even attempted to touch, the bulk of the populations concerned.

However, government and technical services in the colonies were directed, and to a large degree performed, by officials and experts trained in the homelands of the colonial powers. Most of the

industries, communications, transport, banks, large trading establish-
ments, dams, and irrigation works were built, directed and supervised down to the foreman level by foreigners trained in more
advanced countries . There has probably never been any informed
estimate of the numbers of Western-trained officials, administrators,
technicians and teachers (excluding the military) serving in the
colonies, but surely at the height of the empire, say around 1910,
they numbered at least between 100,000 and 200,000, and surely
the annual flow was on the order of 10,000 to 20,000.

The sudden disintegration of the colonial system brought about
the abrupt departure of thousands of foreign administrators and
technicians from the newly independent countries, and the gradual
withdrawal over subsequent years of thousands more from both
government and private services. More serious, the countries were
left with few local training and research institutions, and the flow
of outside administrators and experts was reduced to a trickle. This
happened at a time when hundreds of millions of people expected a
sharp improvement, not deterioration, in their conditions of life.

The foundations of empire had been undermined by World War II,
but the edifice still stood at war's end and there is little evidence that
those who created the United Nations had any conception that the
colonial system would crumble with such speed. As the empires
crashed and independent nations arose, the United States, the
Soviet Union, and a few other countries moved by instinct and
calculation to help fill the desperate need for capital and technical
assistance. And slowly at first, but with increasing momentum, the
United Nations has moved to help the new nations build the foundations of their national independence, for it was clear that some
rational, non-political substitute for the services rendered by the
colonial powers was imperative. But the U.N. agencies have only
started, and their resources are still far from adequate to do the
job that needs doing.

FAO has had especially heavy responsibilities because colonial
administrators did so little to provide the services necessary to
modernize agriculture in territories overwhelmingly agricultural.
In most of the colonies private foreign interests developed planta-

tions, and foreign individuals created a relatively few modern, thriving farms. But these had very little impact upon native farming, which continued as it had for centuries. The gap between primitive and modern agriculture — a gap which needs filling with knowledge, research and training institutions, and capital — is therefore colossal.

From one to two would seem to be a simple, minimum, and innocent progression. But when those figures are percentages, when they denote *annual* increases in the world's population, and when they are applied to 3 billion *people*, the progression mushrooms into the most appalling and revolutionary force ever to hit the human race. This means 60 million new people on earth each year, and if today's rate of increase continues, it means 6 billion people on earth 35 years hence: two persons for every one now.

This is a totally new problem for the human race, and it has arisen largely in the last 20 years. It stems not from any marked increase in birth rates, but from modern miracle drugs and insecticides, combined with massive world-wide public health programs, which have nearly halved death rates: more babies survive and more older people live longer.

The 2 per cent annual population increase is a world average, and includes North America, Western Europe, the U.S.S.R., the Communist states of Eastern Europe, Japan, and a few other countries where the annual increase is less than 2 per cent. In nearly all the countries of Asia, Africa, and Latin America, population is increasing at rates ranging from 2 to 3 per cent each year. At $2\frac{1}{2}$ per cent, a population doubles in 27.6 years, at 3 per cent, in 23.1 years, and at 4 per cent, in 17.3 years. Two-thirds of the peoples on earth live in those continents, and those 2 billions of people, with average incomes of $100 a year, have come for the first time in history to expect rapid improvement in their conditions of life. Their governments as well as the governments of the richer countries are committed to help bring this about. But without a deliberate reduction in today's rates of population increase the hopes of two-thirds of the people on earth for a better life are doomed to frustration.

If the world could be ruled efficiently by a dictator (which is not possible), if there were no separate states with political or economic boundaries, and if modern science and statecraft were applied with sufficient intensity on a world-wide scale to produce and distribute food, certainly the expected numbers of people on earth could be fed for some time to come, certainly to the year 2000. But we do not live in that kind of world and are not likely to do so. Ignorance, hunger, and malnutrition reign in the countries where two-thirds of the world's people live, and present national and international effort is barely succeeding in preventing the situation from worsening. In some countries even this effort is not succeeding.

Economic and social improvement in underdeveloped countries requires greater investment in agriculture, industry, education, and public works, and most of the investment must come from local savings. It also demands greatly increased expenditures for public services and more effective government administration. Present high birth rates operate to reduce savings and *per capita* income. They produce high percentages of dependent children, who consume but do not produce. They increase the financial burden of education and other public services. They increase population pressure on already densely settled land and thus reduce capacity to save and the possibilities of escape from the poverty trap by succeeding generations. High birth rates increase underemployment, create over-crowding, promote disease, undermine health, and thereby reduce productivity. Low productivity means low income and savings.

During the 1950's development programs in Asia, Africa, and Latin America, aided by substantial foreign aid and investment, succeeded in bringing about an average economic growth rate of 3 per cent a year. With population increasing at about 2 per cent a year, the annual increase in *per capita* income was therefore only about 1 per cent. In December 1961 the United Nations declared the 1960's to be a Development Decade and set as a goal the attainment by 1970 in each underdeveloped country of a 5 per cent annual growth rate. To increase the economic growth rate from 3 to 5 per cent in 10 years a country would have to increase national income by 50 per cent and it is highly doubtful that many poor countries can achieve it. In fact, as of today — 1965 — not many are on the way to doing so. But even if they do achieve it, there will be very little improvement in living conditions in countries where population is rapidly growing, because most of the increase in national income will merely provide for the increased population at the same standard. For a country whose population is increasing by 2 per cent a year and whose *per capita* income is now $100, attainment of the U.N. goal by 1970 will mean a *per capita* increase to only $123; if the population rises by 3 per cent a year, the *per capita* income will increase to only $111 in 1970.

Clearly, even with more foreign aid and investment, economic and social progress is going to be very slow, if at all possible, in countries where population is mounting at today's rates. With the industrialized countries growing steadily richer, with living conditions for the average family in less developed countries improving almost imperceptibly, and with population pressures on land, living space and frontiers mounting, the world is in for trouble.

But what about the possibilities of birth control? In only one country, Japan, have conscious efforts effectively reduced the rate of population increase — from 2 to 1 per cent in the postwar period. The governments of India, Pakistan, Egypt and Tunisia recognize the problem and are moving, even though inadequately and without significant numerical results, toward meeting it. Elsewhere in the three underveloped continents the problem is either ignored or receiving only token recognition or action.

Even if birth rates should decrease dramatically tomorrow, which is definitely not in prospect, population growth would not show significant declines for several decades. In the countries of Asia, Africa, and Latin America, children under the age of 15 constitute from 37 to 42 per cent of the total population. While that group is passing through the child-producing ages, natural increases will continue to be high even if family size is reduced. Moreover, infant and child mortality is continuing to decline and this will tend to sustain the proportion of young people. Most demographers believe that under no circumstance will the rate of population growth fall below 1.7 per cent a year during the next 30 to 40 years.

These facts are alarming to those concerned with how, and how well, the increasing numbers of people on earth are going to be nourished. For it has been learned that food production can be effectively increased in a country only as a sector, however important, of overall economic and social development.

There are more hungry and badly nourished people on earth than ever before in history. This fact towers in our time above the astonishing achievements of science and technology, revolutionized transport, intensified national agricultural programs, and existing efforts of wealthier countries, through the United Nations and otherwise, to transfer knowledge, skills, and capital to the poorer. The situation has not improved in the last 5 years. In fact, it has deteriorated.

The compilation and study of statistics on hunger and malnutrition is a vast enterprise which has burgeoned in the last 20 years with FAO playing the leading role. The most striking end-product of a great amount of labor in this field is the conclusion that from 10 to 15 per cent of the people in the world as a whole are positively, consciously hungry, that another 30 to 35 per cent do not get enough of the right kinds of foods to keep them vigorous and healthy, and that of the world's people, up to half suffer from hunger or malnutrition or both.

The problem of mass hunger and malnutrition is one which affects the countries of Asia, Africa, and Latin America. When FAO published its first *World Food Survey*, in 1946, it measured food "adequacy" only against a uniform standard of 2600 calories per person per day. In its second *Survey* published in 1952 it was able to measure food adequacy country by country and against a more scientific calorie-requirement scale, adequacy varying according to climate, labor, habits, and according to more complex food values. The third and latest *Survey* published in 1962 used even more refined techniques to determine diet adequacy, and household food consumption surveys were used to refine conclusions on nutrition. According to this study, the *average* calorie intake in the underdeveloped countries as a whole is 2150 per day compared with

3050 in the richer countries, and it is concluded that 20 per cent of the people in the underveloped countries are by any standard under-fed. The nutritional picture is even worse. Sixty per cent of the households derive more than 80 per cent of their calories from cereals, starchy roots and sugar. This means, according to accepted medical standards, definite undernourishment leading to lack of vigor and a variety of disabling diseases. The amount of animal protein intake in the poorer countries is only one-fifth of that of the richer countries.

The prospects for improvement are not encouraging. For 5 years running, world agricultural production as a whole has failed to make any headway at all against growing population. In other words, there has been no *per capita* increase in agricultural production, and therefore no margin for improvement in nutrition and living levels. In fact, in the 1963–4 season, the increase in world agricultural production fell slightly behind world population in-crease.

But these are *world* figures. They include production in Western Europe, North America, and Australia and New Zealand where output continues to increase more than population and where people are already more than well-fed. The situation is far more disturbing when the other regions are considered separately.

On average, the people of Latin America and the Far East eat far less well today than they did before World War II. Their food supply dropped sharply during the war, and in only one exceptionally favorable year has it been as high as before the war. More serious is the fact that after improvement during the middle 1950's, *per capita* production in Latin America has declined each year for 5 years, and in the Far East for 3 years. Food production there is simply not keeping up with population growth. This is especially serious for the Far East where half the people of the world live and where most people have always existed near the brink of starvation. Agricul-tural production in Egypt has shown a satisfactory and almost unbroken increase during the last 10 years, but elsewhere in the Near East sharp year-to-year fluctuations, depending upon rainfall, have shown no particular trend. There has been a steep 10-year downward trend in production *per capita* in Northwest Africa, and very little recorded change in Africa south of the Sahara.

Unless food production increases at a considerably higher rate than population, the hopes and expectations of the people of three continents for better conditions of life are vain. Reasonable improvements in the quantity and quality of their diets will require over the next 10 years an 80 per cent gain in total food supplies and a 120 per cent rise in production of animal products. Looking ahead 35 years to the year 2000, when world population is expected to be around 6 billions, the underdeveloped countries will have to increase their total food supplies fourfold, and their supplies of animal products sixfold if their people are to be fed adequately. This is a staggering prospect, a goal which at the rates of today's production and population growth is not going to be even approached. But is it, from a technical point of view, even *possible* of attainment?

World potentials for increasing food production are very large indeed. But as pointed out in FAO's basic study *Possibilities for Increasing Food Production*, "it does not serve much purpose to attempt to answer such a question on a global basis. It is unlikely that imports of food from the wealthier to the less wealthy regions can ever provide more than a small part of the needs. This would still remain true even if commercial imports were supplemented by substantial grants-in-aid through free distribution of surplus foodstuffs. It is therefore necessary to examine this question region by region."

The FAO study is concerned almost exclusively with estimates of physical resources and their potentialities for greater yields. Conclusions regarding the several regions are as follows:

> In Latin America and Africa, the physical resources are unquestionably ample, without approaching their full utilization, to meet the estimated (food) increases required. . . . The outcome will depend primarily upon the establishment of progressive and stable governments that are willing and able to mobilize their own resources and make effective use of foreign aid. The rate of resource destruction in some parts of Africa is, however, cause for considerable concern. . . .
>
> In the Near East, an increase in production in excess of threefold would push utilization of resources much closer to the limits set by present technical knowledge. . . . Quite apart from the political,

administrative and institutional problems involved, it is an area in which there may be cause for some disquiet from the point of view of the natural resources. Water is strictly the limiting factor. . . . Of course, all this might be changed by the desalinization of sea water at costs which would be economic for irrigation, though transportation costs to areas far removed from the coast could still remain a problem. The need for a more than fourfold increase in food production in the Far East definitely raises the question of the adequacy of the basic physical resources. . . .

It is emphasized in the FAO study that these conclusions are based solely upon technical factors and potentialities, but that non-technical factors are basic and to a large degree controlling:

> Disease and malnutrition, lack of elementary education, ignorance, superstition and distrust of change, poverty often so absolute that it leaves the farm family nothing to invest in improvements and not daring to risk innovations, very small and fragmented holdings, adverse tenure relations, bad taxation systems, poor credit facilities, poor marketing and processing outlets, lack of domestic capital for investment in improved methods, political instability and sometimes even military turmoil, administrative inefficiency and corruption, shortage of trained personnel for technical leadership and administration and, above all, inadequate government services for agricultural research, education and extension — these are the difficulties of an under-developed country.

It was only about 15 years ago that men's minds began to consider systematically the ways and means by which backward, predominantly agricultural countries could most effectively and quickly advance toward the modern world and narrow the gap between the richer and poorer countries. The science and methodology of country development are therefore new and rapidly evolving. There have been passing fashions, considered at the time as ultimate truths but later modified or superseded, and many mistakes have been made. Given the scope and complexity of the problems involved, this was inevitable. But as "the most hopeful enterprise of our time" has gathered momentum, the methodology of development has acquired a wider and more solid base, and a few reasonably firm conclusions have been reached.

Ten years ago, overwhelming emphasis was placed upon industrialization as the cure for poverty in the underdeveloped countries — industrialization which would siphon off surplus labor from the farms and provide the basis for self-sustaining economic growth. Since then experience and studies, while not overruling that basic conclusion, have profoundly modified it. Here are some of the facts which are being taken into account:

In most underdeveloped countries much more than half — up to 80 per cent — of the total population earns its living by agriculture.

The labor force in these countries, most of it in agriculture, is increasing at rates between 2 and 4 per cent each year. A decrease in the birth rate would have no effect upon the labor force for 15 years and only minor effect for at least three decades.

In underveloped countries, which start from a very small industrial base, even a process of industrialization far more rapid than is now taking place cannot for several decades ahead provide outlets for the underutilized labor force. In fact, industrialization may for decades release more labor than it employs, especially if the industries are modern, labor-saving, fairly large-scale, and replace existing traditional handcraft and other labor-intensive production.

Unless there is very careful planning and control, and unless industrialization takes place in the context of a much wider social and economic progress, small and profitable industrial enclaves could be built up, as in colonial times, without benefiting the larger economy which could be left backward and stagnating.

The forms of industrialization which should be given highest priority are those whose benefits accrue to agriculture, to industries which use or process local products of the land, sea, and forest, either for export or as substitutes for imports. This would increase and conserve foreign exchange required to pay for increased imports needed for industrialization.

Industrialization is without question essential, but it is even more important to increase radically and rapidly the productivity of labor and the efficiency with which labor is applied to the land, the forests, and the seas and rivers. This will require land reform, and revolutionary changes in the attitudes to life and work of the masses of poverty-stricken peasants on the farms.

Greater agricultural productivity is essential to industrialization. But equally, agricultural productivity can be improved only in the context of overall economic and social development which includes industrialization and education. For progress in any one sector, including agriculture, development planning covering *all* sectors of the economy is absolutely essential.

Agriculture is now recognized as holding a major key to world development. But the job of modernizing agriculture in three continents is fearful to contemplate. Even to describe the problem is not simple. Doing something effective about it is the hardest task ever undertaken by civilization.

The "most hopeful enterprise of our time" is hopeful chiefly because we have begun to appreciate the task ahead and are beginning, as will be seen in the subsequent parts of this book, to tackle it.

PART II

The United Nations at Work

CHAPTER I

IS THERE A UNITED NATIONS FAMILY?

SOMEWHERE in the Atlantic, in a world convulsed in war, President Franklin D. Roosevelt and Prime Minister Winston Churchill met on a battleship and spotlighted for the world the two most essential conditions of peace: freedom from fear and want. This conception contained in the Atlantic Charter of 12 June 1942 fired imaginations throughout the world and in effect fixed the ultimate goals of post-war planning. As interpreted during the war years these conditions for peace came to mean collective security against aggression, respect by governments for human rights, and continuous battle against hunger, disease, ignorance and poverty. Moreover, they were interpreted as meaning a continuous flow of investment capital from the richer to the poorer nations to assure rising standards of living, stability in the world monetary exchanges, and a freeing of international trade from strangling restrictions. Finally, they meant the creation of international organizations through which the nations would work continuously to create and maintain those conditions of peace.

Thus, the nations which had been loosely "united" for winning the war proceeded to shape a *family of organizations* to help create and maintain the conditions of peace. The family today includes the pre-eminent U.N. Organization in New York with its General Assembly, three Subsidiary Councils, and Secretariat, with overall responsibilities for world peace and well-being. It also includes a number of Specialized Agencies which work intensively in specific fields, such as food and agriculture, health, education, cultural relations, investment, monetary stability, air transport, labor standards, and peaceful use of atomic energy. Today the Specialized Agencies in the U.N. family number fourteen (see the list below), including four international organs in existence in one form or another long before the war which were adopted into the U.N. family.

In addition to the Specialized Agencies, the family as it has grown over the years includes four other members about whom we shall be hearing a great deal in this book because they have money (or food or equipment), which is spent in cooperation with FAO and a number of the other U.N. agencies. These four were established by the U.N. General Assembly and are separately administered, but their resources are contributed by individual countries for special U.N. purposes and are outside the regular U.N. budget: the Expanded Program of Technical Assistance (EPTA); the U.N. Special Fund (UNSF); U.N. Children's Fund (UNICEF), and the World Food Program (WFP).

UNITED NATIONS FAMILY

Specialized Agencies	*Symbol*
Food and Agriculture Organization of the United Nations	FAO
International Labour Organization	ILO
U.N. Educational Scientific and Cultural Organization	UNESCO
World Health Organization	WHO
International Development Association	IDA
International Bank for Reconstruction and Development	IBRD
International Finance Corporation	IFC
International Monetary Fund	IMF
International Civil Aviation Organization	ICAO
Universal Postal Union	UPU
International Telecommunication Union	ITU
World Meteorological Organization	WMO
Inter-governmental Maritime Consultative Organization	IMCO
International Atomic Energy Agency*	IAEA

* The International Atomic Energy Agency for technical reasons declines to be called a Specialized Agency; however, it is like the others in all important respects, except that it is not subject to the coordinating role of the U.N. Economic and Social Council but is directly under the General Assembly and the Secretary-General.

Some other important members of the family

World Food Program	WFP
U.N. Children's Fund	UNICEF
Expanded Program of Technical Assistance	EPTA
U.N. Special Fund	UNSF

The parents of all the members of the U.N. family are the sovereign nations who united to create them, and each member is the product of the same urge to keep the peace and promote human welfare. Nevertheless, each is the result of a separate initiative, a response to a special need.

Each of the Specialized Agencies is separately chartered by the founding governments. Each has its independent budget voted and supported by member countries. Each is governed by a conference or assembly at which all member countries are represented and an executive council or board consisting of a small group of them which meets more frequently. And each has its own secretariat with a head elected by member countries. Each secretariat quite naturally has developed an institutional loyalty and pride, but what is perhaps more significant and less well known is that the delegates which national governments regularly send to represent them in the governing conference of a particular agency also tend to develop a parochial loyalty to that agency.

According to a requirement of the U.N. Charter each of the Specialized Agencies is "related" to the United Nations, New York, by means of a negotiated, ratified agreement. The United Nations is empowered in its Charter "to make recommendations for the coordination of the policies and activities of the Specialized Agencies" and in fact does so through the Economic and Social Council and an Administrative Committee on Coordination operating directly under the Secretary General. The United Nations recognizes that much of the work of improving economic and social conditions in the world is carried out by the Specialized Agencies.

Is, then, this assemblage of U.N. organizations a real family? If you ask this question of almost any official of the United Nations or one of the agencies he is likely to reply with a wry smile, and if encouraged he may show you his scars. But invariably he will add "I hope so." Actually, the answer to this question depends upon one's experience with family life. If your family circle has been small and your family life orderly and sheltered, with legitimacy unquestioned and central authority maintained, you may not consider the U.N. family of organizations is a real family. But, if you have known a big family of headstrong adults, engaged in varying professions, some living in the family homestead and some in homes of their own, some financially dependent and others with varying degrees of financial independence; if you have known the competitiveness and hard words that can temporarily disrupt a large family circle, but at the same time the affection, the camaraderie, and above all the deeper loyalty and common purpose which infuses and binds it; if you have known and felt these things, then you will affirm as I do that there is a U.N. family.

In the early postwar years, it is true, the group did not appear to be a family and scarcely operated as one. Intra-family relations were few. There was friendly consultation, but little more. Each member, operating on a relatively small budget, took pride in its independence and technical competence, each had its own job to do, and there was relatively little need for using each other, and depending upon each other such as usually occurs in a family. But this early pattern of relationships scarcely had time to gather the moss of tradition before the current world events began to force change in the activities of the United Nations and the Specialized Agencies, to increase the scope and alter the character of the organizations concerned, and to transform profoundly the relations between them.

Those who planned the postwar international machinery thought they had provided nearly everything needed, and at the time their plans seemed adequate and far-seeing. But even as plans were being translated into organized activity it became evident that serious miscalculations had been made. Production and trade (farm to market, city to farm, country to country) were found to be disorganized and demoralized far beyond anticipation, hunger and food shortage throughout the world were far more rampant, and history was moving faster and more brutally than anyone could have imagined. The cold war assumed the proportions of an unrelieved blizzard. Reconstruction and recovery ground to a stop in Western Europe in January and February of 1947 calling forth from the United States massive assistance in the form of the Marshall Plan for a European Recovery Program, unanticipated and outside U.N. channels. Meanwhile the world's colonial empires were disintegrating at a pace and with consequences unforeseen, yielding to inexperienced, independent national states from which colonial administrators, experts, settlers and businessmen were withdrawing in droves.

Neither the world's postwar planners nor the United Nations and the agencies appear to have realized fully in their first years of operations the extent of the need for a massive transfer of knowledge and skills from the richer, advanced, industrialized countries to the majority less fortunate. There were of course a few individuals crying in the wilderness, but the idea does not seem to have caught on that if the poorer nations of the world, containing two-thirds of the human race, were to make any significant headway against human want they were going to have to have, among other things, experts from the more advanced countries come and help them increase production and productivity, survey and develop their resources, establish research and training institutions, and plan and execute development programs.

Almost from its beginning, the United Nations carried on through its secretariat in New York a very small program of technical assistance in the fields of economic development planning, social welfare, and public administration. But with the exception of WHO, which came into being only late in 1948 and which from the first was geared for technical assistance and had substantial funds for it, the other agencies even as late as 1950 were not in a position to render technical assistance on any significant scale. They, like the U.N. Organization itself, were designed to promote economic and social advancement chiefly by means of research, technical studies, publications, conferences, consultations, and stimulation and coordination of action by governments.

FAO was a good case in point. Its intellectual fathers had foreseen the need for direct technical assistance to less developed countries in the improvement of agriculture, fisheries and forestry, and the FAO Charter had authorized it. But the governing conference had not voted any money for it. With $1,140,000 unexpectedly inherited from the expiring U.N. Relief and Rehabilitation Administration in 1947, FAO gave agricultural advisory help in nine countries, and contrived from its regular budget to carry out several other study and advisory missions, but it was increasingly besieged with requests for help to which it could not respond. Even in late 1950 FAO activities were confined largely to headquarters. There were three skeleton regional offices chiefly for contact with governments. Virtually no technical experts, other than those mentioned above, had been supplied to governments. The total staff numbered 507, of which 129 were technical specialists. Of a total budget of $5 million, only $171,780 was spent on travel, conference and consultations. FAO was like a body without arms and legs to go to the aid of nations which most needed its help, and the same was true of other U.N. agencies.

In late 1948 it became clear to those in Washington concerned with foreign policy that the United States was going to have to act to help Latin America, Asia and Africa along the road of progress. With the Marshall Plan under way, Western Europe was by that time on the first rung of the recovery ladder, but Asia, Africa and Latin America were floundering and no help was in sight. There was a modest clamor for a "Marshall Plan for Asia", but this was out of the question, for the Marshall Plan pattern was not suitable. *Re*construction was needed in Asia, but even more that continent needed, as did Africa and Latin America, *con*struction, in other words a development of resources requiring, as a foundation, knowledge and skills and organization that had never existed there on a scale wide enough to attract sufficient capital. So in the famous Point IV of his Inaugural Address on 20 January 1949, President Truman launched the concept of transferring to the underdeveloped areas of the world the benefits of modern science and technology. His conception struck fire because it responded accurately to a need which many sensed and felt but which few dared even to recognize.

The President's words have been quoted often, but they merit re-

reading for they are more meaningful today than when he spoke them 15 years ago:

> We must embark on a bold new program for making the benefits of our scientific advances and industrial progress available for the improvement and growth of underdeveloped areas. . . .
>
> I believe that we should make available to peace-loving peoples the benefits of our store of technical knowledge in order to help them realize their aspirations for a better life. And, in cooperation with other nations, we should foster capital investment in areas needing development.
>
> Our aim should be to help the free peoples of the world, through their own efforts, to produce more food, more clothing, more materials for housing, and more mechanical power to lighten their burdens.
>
> We invite other countries to pool their technological resources. . . . This should be a cooperative enterprise in which all nations work together through the United Nations and its specialized agencies wherever practicable. It must be a worldwide effort for the achievement of peace, plenty, and freedom.

The President's Point IV was destined to have the most profound consequences for three continents, to revolutionize the operations of many of the members of the U.N. family of organizations, and to transform profoundly the relations between them. This we shall see in succeeding chapters.

CHAPTER 2

THE UNITED NATIONS SENDS PEOPLE TO HELP

PRESIDENT TRUMAN, enormously pleased with the enthusiastic world response to his Point IV, lost no time in proposing action. He had launched the idea publicly on 20 January 1949 in his Inaugural Address. When the U.N. Economic and Social Council (ECOSOC) met less than three weeks later, the U.S. delegate, Mr. Warren Austin, promptly submitted a resolution, approved by the Council on 4 March, calling for the preparation of a comprehensive plan for technical assistance. Such a plan was prepared and approved by ECOSOC and the U.N. General Assembly during the year. And at a pledging conference held in June 1950, fifty-four governments pledged $20 million to be allocated to the agencies according to a formula worked out by ECOSOC.

Thus, with U.S. initiative was launched the U.N. Expanded Program of Technical Assistance* for economic development, another "unsordid" enterprise which, even if it did not merit the superlative understatement which Sir Winston Churchill applied to the Marshall Plan, ranked high in imagination and daring. No great debates or stormy international meetings preceded, and no drama attended its launching. No sums of money large enough to excite public attention have ever been involved: the annual resources of the fund have increased slowly over the years from about $20 million contributed by 58 countries in 1950-1, to $51 million contributed by 104 countries in 1964. Even the U.S. contribution of about 40 per cent of the total is so small that few people outside the government offices and Congressional Committees directly con-

---

* So named because it was considered an expansion of the very small technical assistance program already carried on by the U.N. Secretariat.

cerned in Washington are aware of it. Nevertheless, operating quietly, the Expanded Program of Technical Assistance (which shall henceforth be referred to as EPTA) is one of the most meaningful undertakings of our time. In addition to the world work it has made possible directly, it has helped stimulate world thought and initiative leading to still other U.N. undertakings such as the U.N. Special Fund which, together with EPTA, may occupy more space in future histories than the Marshall Plan.

EPTA breathed new life into the U.N. family of organizations, gave its members mobility, endowed them in effect with field services, enabled them to respond on the spot to urgent calls for help in meeting the problems crowding in upon them. But EPTA did more. It enabled the agencies to select and send abroad for training many thousands of promising young men who would return to their countries better equipped to do their jobs and to train others. Before EPTA, most of the agencies were obliged, in effect, to respond to calls for help by correspondence. Now, they could send knowledgeable administrators and technicians.

To FAO and its aims, EPTA seemed heaven-sent. The world was clamoring for food. EPTA gave FAO the means with which to go into the world and do what governments had been asking for and what the headquarters staff had felt all along FAO it should be doing, that is, show governments and people how to grow more and better food. Because of the overwhelming importance of food, agriculture, forestry and fisheries in the underdeveloped countries, FAO received initially the largest share of EPTA funds — 29 per cent. And when country contributions to the fund began to flow in the autumn of 1950, FAO was early off the starting line and into the field because, in anticipation of funds, FAO had been inundated by governments with requests for help and already had quite a number of projects agreed upon, ready to go. A year later FAO, with its financial resources increased from the $5 million a year of its regular budget to more than $10 million by the addition of the new U.N. funds, had work under way on a hundred projects in 35 countries, involving 213 scientific and professional experts of 32 nationalities.

During the years 1950–63 EPTA received from governments $400 million, permitting the agencies to furnish nearly 29,000 "man-years" (one man for a year) of technical assistance to 133 countries and territories. During those same years EPTA furnished FAO alone with $100 million with which it supplied 8000 man-years in technical assistance to needy countries. The FAO experts were recruited from ninety different countries and territories. EPTA funds also made it possible during the same period for the U.N. agencies to select over 26,000 fellows and send them abroad for training. Of these over 3000 were selected and sent by FAO. In addition to paying the agencies for the direct costs of experts and fellows, EPTA pays them an additional 12 per cent to cover technical supervision and servicing by headquarters.

It is a pity that the varied, frequently dramatic, always interesting activity with which we are here concerned should be dried out and reduced to dust by the appellation "technical assistance"; that the intensely human beings involved, once they are dubbed experts, are drained of blood and human warmth; that figures such as $50 million for technical assistance, 26,000 man-years and 24,000 fellows, convey so little meaning; and that an important source of funds for an exciting human world activity should be saddled with as discouraging a name as ever repelled interest or inquiry: The Expanded Program of Technical Assistance! If technical assistance is a bore, a program of technical assistance is a colossal bore, and an expanded program is an expanded colossal bore. Human activity engaged in international aid and development seems to have outrun the capacity of language to describe it. The gobbledegook of international development may be adequate to convey thoughts between professionals (it frequently seems doubtful), but it long ago left even the thoughtful general reader behind. Thus, non-professionals are usually excluded from the drama of aid and development, and aid and development are denied the public appreciation and support they deserve.

I confess I have been unimpressed over the years by the modest financial figures representing EPTA financing of technical assistance by the U.N. family. Being inured, as many people are, to annual

battles in the U.S. Congress over U.S. "foreign aid" and whether a
$4.5 billion "aid" program should be cut to $4 billion or $3 billion,
I have tended to consider EPTA and the U.S. contribution of $10
million to $20 million a year as almost insignificant. Actually, when
you shear away from the U.S. aid figures the enormous sums for
military aid, defense support, budget support, equipment and
supplies, and consider technical assistance *per se*, the United States
in its bilateral programs provides far less technical assistance than
the U.N. family (though the family enjoys generous U.S. financial
support, to be sure!). I have also over the years seen the figures of
EPTA-financed numbers of experts on the job — nearly 3000
today — and they have left me cold: what can so few do that could
affect significantly the problems of two-thirds of the world?

Technical assistance rendered by experts! It sounds like something done by mechanical creatures with metal tools. But technical
assistance is just plain help, and an expert is a warm-blooded human
being who, because of specialized training and experience, knows
more about getting a particular job done than the people he is
helping. An expert in the international assistance business is no
more nor less compassionate than anybody else and he is seldom
"dedicated" in either the complimentary or pejorative usage of the
word. But he *is* always professional, and as such, confronted with
a challenging job, he frequently throws himself into it with enthusiasm and intensity. He may have gone abroad for any number of
reasons, perhaps to get away from a restricted college community or
a nagging wife, but once engaged, it is his professional interest and
pride which drive him.

The expert sent by the United Nations goes at a government's
invitation. At least part of his local costs are provided by the
government, and he usually works alongside a local person who
either has some competence in the same field or aspires to gain some.
The expert may be invited to advise on the solution of a particular
problem, or to help organize an activity, or to lecture and train, or
to survey a wide situation and to recommend policies. His activities
directly and deeply influence at least one or several people, or up to
hundreds or thousands of people at second hand. But his scope and

influence are unpredictable, depending upon his personality and local circumstances. He may very well be, and not infrequently is, the catalyst for government action of the broadest and most far reaching kind, in fields far beyond his technical speciality. Political problems which obstruct progress, and even international impasses, may, and sometimes do, yield as a consequence of his quiet wisdom. Thus, the expert may influence government policies affecting millions.

In Cairo I was talking one day with a modest but merry-eyed Irishman, a leading expert on water resources, who had been sent on repeated assignments by FAO. I was trying with little success to pry some information out of him as to what he had done, when in walked a vigorous Egyptian colonel, a senior official in Egypt's Desert Development Authority. He greeted the Irishman as a long-lost friend, was introduced to me and, with his arm around my friend's shoulder, asked me, "Do you know what this fellow did for us?" I allowed that I had been trying to find out without much success. "Well", the colonel said, "he came out here several years ago, sent by FAO, and made a study of ground water down in New Valley. As a result of his advice we went ahead and are developing the whole area."

"How long did he stay?"

"Only two or three weeks."

"But what could he do in only two or three weeks that was of such importance?"

"He gave us confidence. We had some ideas but were not at all sure. We knew that this man was good, and when he said we had enough good water there we went ahead. We ask him to come back for consultation now and then, and he comes. He is responsible for the job we're doing."

The colonel later filled my ear with stories of half a dozen other instances in which FAO expert help had been crucial to the work of the Desert Development Authority. "I was once told", he said, "that FAO experts only came, wrote reports which we filed, and then went away. This is not so. You have to learn how FAO works, but once you do, they continue to work *with* you, and there's no end to what you can do together."

I heard the same story at the Ministry of Agriculture in Cairo, where praise for U.N. experts was astonishingly generous. There are not many activities relating to food and agriculture in Egypt where U.N. experts are not credited with crucial contributions.

"You of course know about C. L. Pan, don't you?" asked one of the Ministry's senior officials. "He's a Hong Kong Chinese that FAO sent here several years ago. He stayed quite a while and developed and adapted to our conditions a new corn hybrid. Egypt used to import a lot of corn. Now we not only supply our own needs but corn is one of our important exports."

And "You've met Koshal, haven't you? He's a statistical genius FAO sent us — now attached to the Ministry — probably the best in the world at estimating crops by sampling — all crops, and fruits and milk too. We've set up a new unit to estimate crops by the methods he's developed. We've revised our whole system of crop reporting and are now training people from other countries in his methods. Oh, he's a dynamo. He can't keep a chauffeur very long because he works him about twenty hours a day. Sleeps travelling in the car and every time he wakes up tells the chauffeur to drive faster."

I did meet R. S. Koshal later, and the genius from India was indeed a dynamo.

Chile is a long way from Egypt, but dozens of U.N. experts recruited by FAO have been there too. When the managing director of the Chile Development Corporation received me in his modern office in Santiago it was clear from his brisk manner that he was a busy man with no time to waste. "I'll tell you what FAO experts have done for us. Chile now has a forestry policy and we owe it to FAO experts. They came down, a team of them, made a study, recommended a development policy, and we're applying it to the last detail. It's the same with fisheries. We now have a fisheries development policy based upon surveys and recommendations of FAO experts — and we're following it to the letter. It's the same story with livestock development — we have a policy. And in all these cases, FAO experts are now helping us apply the policies. One thing more: FAO experts have been of enormous help to Chile in formulating and passing a land reform law, and are now helping us figure out how to apply it."

Seventeen hundred miles south of Santiago, about as far as you can go on the South American continent, lying along the Straits of Magellan, is Chile's Province of Magellanes which contains, among other things, 10 million acres of windswept grasslands and even more millions of sheep. Twelve years ago the Ministry of Agriculture's research station at Punta Arenas was in charge of a young agronomist named Mario Habit, and it was he who welcomed there an FAO range management expert by the name of Earle D. Sandvig from Portland, Oregon, who had come to advise on what could be done to improve the grasslands and increase wool yields. Sandvig stayed only a few days, but during those days, accompanied by Mario Habit, he visited the leading sheep ranches, including the biggest in the world owned by the Sociedad Exploitadora de Tierra del Fuego, looked over the situation and told the owners and managers what they should do. Then he went away. One of his first acts was to recommend Mario Habit to FAO for a fellowship.

Sitting today in his office in Santiago, directing a nationwide livestock development program, Mario Habit told what happened. "Not long after leaving Punta Arenas, Sandvig wrote me that he felt his trip had been a failure and that he had accomplished nothing. I replied. 'But you have accomplished everything. You have opened our eyes to what can be done.' But I didn't know how much his trip would accomplish later." Then Habit ticked off the later consequences of Sandvig's trip:

Mario Habit received an FAO fellowship and during a year studied modern range improvement practices in the United States, Australia and New Zealand. "And what did that do for you?" I asked. "It gave me knowledge, confidence and prestige," he replied simply.

Upon his return, Habit was hired by the Sociedad Exploitadora de Tierra del Fuego to direct its livestock development program, which included the improvement of 50,000 acres of grasslands each year. The results in wool yields were so spectacular that they attracted the attention of the government and the public. "Everybody in Magellanes will tell you I did this," Habit said, "but I know who is responsible for it — Earle Sandvig."

The Chilean Government's Development Corporation (CORFO) decided to undertake a national livestock development program and asked FAO to send a team of experts to make a study and recommend a policy and a detailed program.* This was done, the program was included in Chile's Ten-Year Plan (it started in 1961), and is being carried into effect with the help of a $20 million World Bank loan. Mario Habit is now directing the program and five FAO experts are serving it as technical advisors.

Such was the influence of an expert in Latin America.

United Nations experts are in Asia, too. A hundred miles or so up country from Bangkok in Thailand, an amiable FAO scientist of French nationality, Dr. H. C. Girard, showed me lovingly around a foot-and-mouth disease laboratory where for several years he had been developing vaccines, making tests, initiating production, and training a staff. Technically an advisor, he was exquisitely deferential toward the handsome young Thai director, but it was clear that not only the director but the entire staff loved him and looked up to him. It was hard to respond unflaggingly to his endless enthusiasm for his viruses, his test mice, his equipment, and the details of his operations, but I tried. Back in Bangkok admiring Thai officials told me that through his efforts they were bringing foot-and-mouth disease under control. They also told me of another FAO man a British subject named J. Hudson, who worked for four years with the Thai Government developing new anti-rinderpest vaccines and new techniques for producing them, with the result that the disease was abolished in Thailand, and also in neighboring Burma. Hudson repeated the performance with a vaccine for hog cholera. An FAO colleague, John Lancaster, also British, did the same with a vaccine which controlled Newcastle disease in poultry. And still another FAO colleague, a Chinese scientist by the name of S. H. Ou, in two

* The importance of livestock development in Chile had been highlighted in a 1952 joint report on agricultural development made by FAO and the World Bank following a joint survey, but their recommendations had not been carried out. Chile, though potentially self-sufficient, imports large quantities of the animal products: meat, wool, milk powder, etc.

years in Thailand made a fundamental contribution to the control of *blast* diseases which attack rice with devastating consequences.

It is frustrating to start giving examples, however briefly, of what individual U.N. experts have done in helping to modernize agriculture, forestry, and fisheries. I can mention here only a tiny fraction of those that I have come across personally in a few countries. There remain in those countries the hundreds of other examples. And beyond those there are the thousands of examples of U.N. experts in a hundred countries which I do not know about at all.

If I have given the impression that all U.N. technical assistance is financed by the EPTA fund it is erroneous. Most of the agencies, including FAO, are able to send a modest number of experts abroad from their own independent budgets. Moreover, they have other sources of United Nations financing for technical assistance, notably the highly important Special Fund, about which we shall hear shortly. But before doing so we should take brief note here of what EPTA did to relations between the members of the U.N. family of organizations.

In brief, the EPTA fund brought about an interlocking of their affairs and required a close cooperation among them which before EPTA had been absent. There was a fund to be divided among the U.N. and the agencies and used by them to achieve a common U.N. purpose.* This naturally required co-ordinating administrative and policy review machinery. So came into being the Technical Assistance Board (TAB) which consists of the heads of the relevant U.N. agencies and an Executive Chairman appointed by the U.N. Secretary-General. This board, the TAB — meaning the agencies themselves together with the Executive Chairman presiding and acting as arbiter — meets three times a year to consider annual requests of governments for help, to study each other's reports on activities already undertaken, and to agree upon an overall program and allocation of funds for the coming year. This

---

* FAO, ILO, WHO, UNTAO, UNESCO, and ICAO receive the bulk of the funds. ITU, WMO and IAEA are smaller purveyors of technical assistance. The World Bank and IMF coordinate their technical assistance activities with the other agencies and may attend meetings of the TAB but do not receive funds from EPTA.

process obviously requires agreement on priorities, and has contributed most importantly over the years to the evolution, enriched and enlightened by operating experience, of a philosophy toward country development.

The decisions of the TAB are, however, only recommendations to the thirty member Technical Assistance Committee (TAC) of the U.N. Economic and Social Council. In TAC representatives of governments make changes as they wish. In the full Economic and Social Council and also in the U.N. General Assembly broad policies are considered. The review and debates in these forums focus attention continuously on world development and the best means for achieving it. Thus new U.N. institutions have been created and new ideas launched, as for example the Development Decade effort of the 1960's.

EPTA funds come from voluntary contributions by governments. Contributions are announced at an annual pledging conference held at U.N. headquarters in New York in the last quarter of each year, during the regular annual session of the General Assembly.

This then, is the U.N. superstructure of coordination, review, and policy determination. But we have ignored thus far the bases of U.N. technical assistance. I have said that the TAB meets "to consider the annual requests of governments". These requests are the foundation stones of the U.N. overall program, but the metaphor is inexact because they are neither dug up nor hewn. They are manufactured, more like cinder blocks, and the mix is complex and variable.

What should a government ask for? The needs of the typical underdeveloped country are endless in nearly every line, its budget limited, and most important of all, its trained and even semi-trained people far too few. Its national development plan, if any, is likely to be rudimentary and the planners inexperienced. For each expert it receives, a country must commit some of its limited funds, its attention, and at least one — usually several — of its promising semi-trained men to work as "counterpart" with the imported specialist. Outside assistance and domestic resources being limited,

C

which needs should be given priority? This is the vital question the country must decide.

Present in the capital city are likely to be representatives of five to ten U.N. agencies, and if the agency representatives are not stationed there, they come there on special missions. Each offers help and each is likely to have a very natural prejudice in favor of his own special field. Likewise present are representatives of various foreign powers, foreign foundations, and private groups, each offering aid. Each offer accepted requires commitment of local time, talent, and resources. What does a government, then, request of EPTA?

To ask these questions is to suggest why, since the early 1950's, most of the givers of aid (certainly the U.N. agencies and the United States) have insisted increasingly upon the importance of national development plans and have made intensive efforts to train local planners. It also suggests why the U.N. agencies have learned increasingly over the years the importance of disciplined coordination of their activities in each country. Finally it suggests why the United Nations (actually the TAB) began to appoint Resident Representatives in the less developed countries and why their number and the importance of their role has increased over the years. Volumes have been written about the developments described in this paragraph and many more doubtless are on the way. The mistakes made in the process of learning, the pulling and hauling, the jealousies — all this we can leave aside here. The important thing is that all concerned learned a great deal about the new business of international development, and are continuing to learn.

Today, the Resident Representative of the Technical Assistance Board has the chief responsibility for coordinating in a given country the activities of the several U.N. agencies having assistance programs there, and for helping the government draw up its annual request for U.N. technical assistance. He is the senior U.N. representative in the country, acknowledged as such by the agencies. It is his job to prevent overlaps or conflicts in projects undertaken in the country by the U.N. agencies, as well as the bilateral aid programs of the United States or other individual countries. In sum, it is his job to help the country make the most effective use of U.N.

assistance in its overall development effort. Seventy-five U.N. Resident Representatives are now stationed in different regions covering over 100 countries.

Up until 1959 when the U.N. Special Fund began operating, U.N. Resident Representatives abroad were appointed by and reported to the Executive Chairman of the TAB, an engaging Englishman, a knowledgeable and effective international civil servant, Mr. David Owen. Since then, the U.N. Resident Representative wears another hat as representative of the U.N. Special Fund, and his appointment is made jointly by Mr. Owen and a close friend of his who occupies a room next door in the gleaming U.N. skyscraper in New York, the dynamic Mr. Paul Hoffman, managing director of the Special Fund. The Resident Representative reports to both. More recently, the Resident Representative has also become country representative of the new U.N./FAO World Food Program.

We shall return to the U.N. Special Fund in the next chapter, but it is perhaps appropriate to add here that in August 1964 the U.N. Economic and Social Council recommended the merger of the Special Fund and EPTA in a single U.N. Development Program, with Mr. Hoffman assuming the title of Administrator and Mr. Owen that of Co-Administrator. When the merger is ratified by the U.N. General Assembly, as expected in the autumn of 1965, the functions exercised by the Governing Council of the Special Fund and the Technical Assistance Committee will be taken over by a single intergovernmental body known as the Governing Council of the U.N. Development Program. For years Mr. Hoffman and Mr. Owen have worked so closely together that their operations were in effect a single program, and in effect there will be little change in administration. However, merger of the governing bodies will simplify procedures and save time and money. Not the least of the benefits of merger will be the disappearance of the confusing and interest-repelling names — EPTA and Special Fund — and the adoption of a simple name which gives a clue to its functions: U.N. Development Program.

CHAPTER 3

THE UNITED NATIONS INVESTS IN KNOWLEDGE

IF the U.N. Expanded Program of Technical Assistance (EPTA), begun in 1950, breathed new life into the U.N. family and gave its members mobility, the U.N. Special Fund which started operations in early 1959 added a wholly new dimension to their activities. And what a dimension: the building of enduring training and research institutions and the foundations for capital investment in half the world! The Special Fund is an expansion and extension of EPTA and the work that was already being carried on by the U.N. agencies. But its conceptions, its scope, and its ground rules are such as to make it in effect a new approach. Paul Hoffman calls it "pre-investment". Special Fund money is used to help governments in three kinds of projects: intensive pre-investment surveys of natural resources and productive capacity leading toward greater public and private investment; support for applied research leading toward the same end; and pre-investment in human beings, the creation or strengthening of institutions which train people to make more effective use of their countries' resources. This is precisely the approach which was most needed at that time for more effective development of the world's lands, forests, and oceans.

Nobody had assumed that the U.N. technical assistance program instituted in 1950 was the whole answer to world development needs. President Truman's Point IV had called for technical assistance *and* increased capital investment. Nevertheless, while technical assistance went ahead, adequate capital flow did not, and there were many years of controversy in the United Nations and elsewhere over capital flow for non-bankable projects such as land reform, water supply, sanitation, pilot housing, health, and institutions for education and training. The debate eventually came to center upon a proposal for the creation of a Special U.N. Fund for Economic Development (SUNFED) which would channel say $200 to $250 millions or more each year from the richer countries of the world to the poorer as grants-in-aid or low interest loans for non-self-liquidating development projects.

SUNFED was strongly opposed by the United States, Great Britain, and the other countries which would be called upon to supply most of the capital. They had no intention of furnishing large sums of money to the United Nations for distribution in ways and for purposes over which they would have no control. Beyond this, they genuinely doubted that, given the dearth of institutions, trained people, and planning in the low income countries, an annual distribution of cash would have any permanent, constructive effect. In fact, they feared most of it would be wasted.

Meanwhile, as the controversy raged, the United Nations and its family of agencies, as well as the countries extending bilateral aid, were learning a great deal about the development business. Obviously technical assistance in the EPTA pattern, though useful and necessary, was not enough. It became distressingly clear that most of the poorer countries were not going to be able to attract domestic or foreign capital until they had help in finding out what their resources were, and until they had institutions capable of training enough people to develop those resources. The aid agencies, and the thousands of technical experts operating around the world during the 1950's in advisory capacities, were increasingly impressed with the need for building enduring local institutions which would acquire knowledge, train people, and survey resources.

As a result of the deadlock in the United Nations on SUNFED and the new insights into development priorities gained over the years, the U.N. General Assembly on 14 October 1958 authorized the creation of the U.N. Special Fund. Forty-one nations pledged $21,500,000 for a first year (pledges for 1959 later reached $26 million). Mr. Paul G. Hoffman was appointed managing director, and in early 1959 the Special Fund began operations.

One cannot help but wonder what would have been the history

of the Special Fund had not the United Nations had the good fortune to get Paul Hoffman to direct it. A man of prodigious reputation (Studebaker Company, Marshall Plan, Ford Foundation), of irresistible charm and persuasiveness, and of inexhaustible energy, Paul Hoffman is here, he is there, he is everywhere, coaxing governments to increase their contributions to the Special Fund, making public speeches about the Special Fund, and relentlessly supervising the far-flung operations of the Fund. Due largely to his efforts, government contributions to the Fund increased annually from $26 million for 1959 to $92 million for 1965. In January 1965, after 6 years of existence, the Special Fund had committed $442 million to 485 separate projects in 130 low income countries and territories. Special Fund money is used for international experts, fellowships, and some equipment and services unavailable locally. The receiving countries had in turn committed to these projects $645 million in local goods, services and cash. The total Special Fund enterprise as of January 1965 involved, therefore, projects totalling $1087 million. More than 2000 experts from all over the world were at work in the field on Special Fund projects, and seventeen of the earlier Special Fund "pre-investments", completed at a cost of $17 million, had attracted "follow-up" investment of some $792 million.

Creation of the Special Fund had the effect of a second stage booster rocket on several of the U.N. agencies, propelling them into development activities of kinds for which they had long seen the need, but for which they had no funds. They were more than ready for the new approach and threw themselves into the work with confidence and enthusiasm.

FAO, which had already grown with EPTA funds from a minor technical organization to a leading technical assistance agency, now became a major world agency for developing land, forests, and oceans. Of the 485 projects negotiated by the Special Fund during the first 6 years of operations, FAO was chosen as executing agency for 195 of them — 40 per cent of the total — for they were in fields of agriculture, water, forests and fisheries in which FAO had superior competence. And of the $442 million committed by the Special

Fund during the period, $168 million were for FAO-executed projects.

The role of the executing agency in a Special Fund extends from beginning to end. The agency helps governments prepare requests to the Special Fund. More than likely the project was suggested informally to the government by an agency in the first place, the idea having grown out of past U.N. technical assistance and other operations in the country. The agency is then involved deeply in all subsequent negotiations which usually entail revisions to meet more fully Special Fund requirements. After the managing director of the Fund and the Fund's Governing Council have approved the project, the agency and the government concerned work out with the Special Fund a detailed plan of operation which is signed by all parties. The negotiations are often long and tedious.

When the plan of operation is finally signed, the agency takes over execution. It appoints a project manager, recruits all experts and procures all equipment needed. Thereafter, it closely supervises operations — with the Special Fund, of course, looking over its shoulder and checking up from time to time. Operations are complex, for the projects are of substantial size (average per project $2.2 million), and extend over several years (average 4 years). To cover expenses of the agency in administering projects, the Special Fund pays the agency 11 per cent on all project costs borne by the Special Fund except the cost of equipment and work done under sub-contract. For equipment, the agency receives 3 per cent, while the amount paid on sub-contracts varies.

The impact of the Special Fund upon the scope and operations of FAO in its land, forest, and ocean development work are suggested by these figures: For the 2 years 1962–3 the FAO total budget for its "Regular Program" was $31,285,000, and for those 2 years FAO received allocations of $21,268,780 from the Special Fund to execute approved projects. For the 2 years 1964–5, the FAO Conference voted a Regular Program budget of $38,838,300, and during that period it is estimated that FAO will receive nearly $48 million in Special Fund allocations.

From New York the projects look like U.N. Special Fund projects and from Rome and often in the field they look like FAO projects. But they are neither. They are the projects of the government which asks for them and which supplies on average 60 per cent of the money and most of the personnel for them. The status of the FAO project manager is that of director or co-director, and all international experts have local counterparts working alongside them. Essential to the whole enterprise, of course, is the idea that when the FAO project manager and the foreign experts withdraw at the end of the project they will leave behind functioning institutions in the hands of men trained to operate them.

Paul Hoffman has solved many complex problems in his professional life, but there is one which completely frustrates him and his staff at U.N. headquarters in New York, and that is how to convey to the public any conception of the dramatic, constructive, worldwide activity being unleashed by the Special Fund. That it cannot be done does not deter him: he continues to try. The 485 tailor-made projects defy meaningful classification or general description. Each involves unique facts, potentialities, hopes and human equations. Each would require for appreciation a separate volume. But then, even if the separate volumes were prepared, who would read them?

The 195 Special Fund projects for which FAO is responsible likewise defy description or more than rudimentary classification. Roughly half of them involve pre-investment surveys of land and water resources. These include soil and soil fertility surveys of whole regions or river basins (qualities of soil, depth, porousness, drainage, suitability for irrigation, chemical properties, response to fertilizers) to determine their crop potentialities. And they include prospecting for underground water, surveys of the possibilities for flood control and irrigation, and reclamation of tidal basins, flood plains, swamps, and deserts.

In addition to land and water use, upwards of thirty-five Special Fund projects executed by FAO are concerned with forest surveys and management, development of forest products industries, and the training of people to carry on essential forest management and development services. Fifteen projects are similarly concerned with fisheries. Thirty-seven involve institution-building and applied research and training in connection with plant and animal breeding and the control of animal and plant diseases. Twenty-five make possible institutional agricultural training, research and extension.

I can perhaps do no better than to mention here several of the Special Fund projects which FAO is executing in Egypt. These examples are no more nor less representative than those found in any other country in a similar stage of advancement, but something may be gained by a conception of the coverage in a single country.

With population growing at the rate of 3 per cent a year and pressing for survival upon that meager 3 per cent of Egypt's land which is arable, the use of modern science and technology in Egypt to increase agricultural productivity is not a matter of choice but of necessity. *All* means must be used: to increase the waters available for irrigation (thus the Aswan Dam!); to increase the productivity of land already irrigated; to discover and make fuller use of ground water; to reclaim tidal areas; to develop semi-arid areas; and to grow more and better poultry and livestock.

In the Nile delta, and increasingly along that fabled river, population pressure is forcing farmers to grow two and sometimes three crops a year on land, now irrigated, which for thousands of years grew only one crop a year following the yearly Nile flooding. As a result the land is becoming water-logged and saline. It never drains or dries out, plants tend to get asphyxiated, and crop yields are going down. This could be remedied by ribbing the fields with drainage canals, but if this were done 15 per cent of the richest land of the Nile delta would be lost to use, and that would be a calamity. What to do? Egypt asked FAO for advice and a Special Fund project was arranged with FAO as executor.

FAO experts in Rome knew that Egypt's problem was not unique, that it exists, among other places, in the Netherlands and has been solved there by digging trenches several feet deep, laying tile pipe sections (or, more recently, perforated plastic pipe) into which water drains at the jointures. The ditches are filled in, the water flows off underground, and cultivation proceeds over the whole area. FAO

...red an expert from a Netherlands engineering firm, ..., a specialist in land drainage, as manager of a 3-year ... to help solve Egypt's problem. The Special Fund is ...ng $365,000 and the Egyptian Government $1 million.

... knowledge and method could not simply take over. It had to be adapted to the soil, the people, the resources of Egypt. What kind of pipe most suitable for Egyptian soil could be made at lowest cost in Egypt? What kind of machinery would be required to make it? Various pipes had to be made, transported and tested in the field. Transport questions had to be studied. Special pipe-laying machines had to be imported and adapted. Administrators, foremen and crews of laborers had to be assembled and trained for large-scale testing and demonstration. Farmers had to be induced to cooperate. The cost of each element and phase had to be calculated and projected to large-scale operation, inasmuch as the Government of Egypt plans underground tile drainage eventually for all its irrigated fields.

Fifty miles northeast of Cairo in the Nile delta my wife and I trudged through wide fields of adhesive black mud to observe a tile-laying machine and crew in action. It was a beautiful, clear day but a cold wind was blowing. Looking from a distance like a huge caterpillar covered and surrounded by moths, the machine was a combination ditch digger and pipe layer which moved along about 15 feet a minute. The moths were a motley crew of farm laborers clad in flapping garments, who are paid about 40 cents a day to carry pipes and water and keep the machine loaded. The pipe sections were ejected evenly in the bottom of the trench. A specially equipped tractor followed, in one operation shoving the soil back into the ditch and leveling it. A camel brought a new load of pipe sections. Would, some day, the whole of irrigated Egypt see what we were then seeing?

The day following, we celebrated the anniversary of the birth of Christ by arising at 6 a.m. and riding in an international truck, accompanied by a learned and charming disciple of Mohammed, Colonel Mohammed Wafik, visiting another FAO Special Fund project in Egypt, this one in the desert. North from Cairo runs the desert road to Alexandria through sand and rock which have never even suspected that mud exists in irrigated land less than a mile to the east. A few miles from the coast one begins to see a little vegetation, so sparse it must be discouraging even to a goat. This is the northwestern coastal region, a narrow strip of land which extends more than 300 miles west of Alexandria to the Libyan border, containing towns whose names evoke such stirring memories of World War II: El Alamein, Mersa Matruh, Sidi Barrani. The strip gets an average of 6 inches of rain a year. In a narrow band extending 3 to 6 miles from the coast, there is enough soil and ground water at shallow depths to allow farmers to cultivate figs, olives, almonds, and some vegetables. Extending south of this band for 15 and occasionally as far as 25 miles there is a catchment area with shallow soil where in years of higher than average rainfall sheep and goats can find feed. Scattered about the area are pockets of land with deep alluvial soil and underground water: there, once every 2 or 3 years, rainfall permits the harvesting of grain crops, and in those years water can be conserved and new soils deposited by the building of earthen dams. The entire region has a population of only about 92,000, mostly nomads whose settlement in permanent farming the Egyptian Government is trying to encourage. Along the coast commercial fishing is slight.

All in all, the area looks inhospitable and, to the untrained observer, impossible to reclaim. Hydrologists and experts in dry farming and range management, however, seem to know better. As for the Government of Egypt, it has no alternative but to attempt to develop the area in order to relieve the growing overcrowding in the Nile delta. By the time the Aswan Dam is finished and its waters put to use on new lands in the south the population will have so increased that the numbers of people living on irrigated land will not have decreased at all. The government has agricultural research stations in the coastal area and has under way a sizeable pilot undertaking for settling nomads, but it needs outside expert help in preparing a plan for developing the whole region. The U.N. Special Fund is therefore contributing $932,200 to provide experts and some equipment for a 3-year pre-investment survey to which the Egyptian

Government is contributing $1,150,000. The project originated in the FAO Regional Office in Cairo, FAO is in charge of the survey, and FAO is recruiting the experts and supplying the equipment needed.

Late that evening we returned to Cairo. We had not seen a single Christmas tree. But we had seen forlorn young fig and almond trees watered from shallow wells by means of bucket and cups. We had seen nomads in all stages of conversion from wanderers to farmers. We had seen flocks of children going to brand-new schools learning to read and write, an art unknown to their parents. And we had seen young agronomists, engineers and administrators happy and full of hope and confidence and faith in the future. That was enough. It was a good Christmas Day.

Far to the south of Cairo in the 2 million acres circling the Aswan–Luxor axis in the Upper Nile, FAO soil experts and their Egyptian colleagues are completing a third Special Fund project: a soil survey. The completion of the High Dam at Aswan will allow a wide extension of irrigation. Which soils are best suited for irrigating which crops? A soil survey is essential if best use is to be made of the precious water.

Egypt is the world's greatest producer of the prized long staple fiber cotton, which is the country's chief export, the basis of a sizeable and growing textile industry, and a mainstay of the Egyptian economy. Egypt is not unsophisticated in cotton technology, the British having established there 30 years ago the world's first cotton fiber laboratory and its first cotton spinning laboratory. One might think that long staple cotton is a simple product, but it is not. Egypt alone grows eight major varieties, all good, and has 30,000–40,000 seed samples whose fiber products vary in purity, spinning performance, and many other qualities. Some 7000–8000 samples are tested in Egypt's laboratory each year for their spinning and ultimate use.

Nevertheless, in an increasingly competitive world, Egypt's cotton technology is in danger of falling behind. Fiber-testing and other laboratory equipment and techniques are growing old-fashioned, and not enough is being done either to develop new breeds or preserve existing ones. There is no adequate classification of Egyptian cottons, no national grading standards so important to export trade, and grading standards are not related closely, as they should be, to breeding and growing. Research is needed to improve ginning efficiency without damage to fibers. And the breeding and distribution of cotton seeds to farmers is not tightly linked up through government organization with cotton ginning, spinning and weaving.

These deficiencies would have the gravest consequences for Egypt if they should continue while world technology advances and other countries forge ahead. The Government of Egypt therefore asked the Special Fund to help finance, equip and launch a modern cotton research laboratory. In charge of the project for FAO is a highly qualified American, Burt Johnson. He and other professionals recruited by FAO to help him will leave behind them, after 4 years, a modern operation and a corps of highly trained people. Incidentally, it is hoped that this laboratory will be so advanced that it will make a research contribution to other cotton growing countries, perhaps including the United States!

The same is expected of the Central Agricultural Pesticides Laboratory which I saw under construction next door to the Ministry of Agriculture in Cairo, and the Vegetable Improvement and Seed Production Centre at Dokki. These are also a joint undertaking of the Government of Egypt, the Special Fund and FAO, designed to serve not only Egypt but all Middle East and to some extent the world. Most pesticides research and testing in the world is done by private manufacturing companies. The new pesticides laboratory in Egypt is a public enterprise which will research, develop and test pesticides and provide technical advice on their manufacture, application, marketing and control. It will study side-effects of pesticides on human beings, wild life and fish. And it will serve as a training center, a source of published information and a stimulus to manufacturing.

The Near East Animal Health Institute, one of whose five branches is in Cairo, illustrates the regional approach to problems which the Special Fund fosters wherever possible. Before the establishment of the regional institute, Iraq, Sudan, Iran, Egypt, and Lebanon were all trying separately, with too little equipment and knowledge and too few trained people, to cope with all of the animal diseases which plague all of them alike. In 1962, following lengthy negotiations with the Special Fund and FAO, the five countries agreed to join in a common regional institute, to divide the work, and to pool their knowledge. Each now focuses on different diseases and each has now expanded research, training, and production of medicines and vaccines in more limited fields. A small central office, located in Beirut, Lebanon, provides communication and liaison among the five. Together they can fight animal diseases more effectively.

Perhaps the most dramatic and publicized Special Fund/FAO activity with which Egypt is concerned, along with thirty-five other countries, is the Desert Locust Project, which illustrates another Special Fund approach. The locust is no stranger to anyone who has read history or the Bible. Breeding fast, traveling faster, clouds of locusts appear seemingly out of nowhere and, ignoring national frontiers, descend upon hapless areas destroying every green thing. In the course of one year locusts destroyed the food of a million people in Ethiopia, and caused $12 million of damage in Morocco in only 6 weeks.

With experts financed by EPTA, FAO started work on the desert locust in the Near East in 1952, studying the problem, advising governments, and promoting cooperative efforts to attack it. At first only one man was engaged in this work, later joined by others. Tirelessly, they traveled the Middle East, South Asia and Africa for years, giving advice and help. But this was not enough. Needed were continuous, preventive measures. Therefore, at an FAO Near East Regional Conference held in Damascus in December 1958, it was decided to ask the Special Fund for help. As a consequence, the Special Fund in 1960 contributed nearly $2.5 million and nineteen governments, including Egypt, contributed nearly $1.4 million for a 6-year program to extend research and training and to develop common policies for preventing locust assaults.

There are now forty-one cooperating countries and territories in the Desert Locust Project. FAO, aided by an international Technical Advisory Committee, administers the money furnished by the Special

Fund and by the governments of eleven countries. It coordinates and directs operations to maintain research stations and create or strengthen national reporting and forecasting services. It also helps governments train personnel and make ecological studies. A team which has included entomologists, plant ecologists, a meteorologist, and a soil specialist, has traveled 75,000 miles during the last few years through Africa, Arabia, India, Pakistan and Iran. A Desert Locust Information Service with headquarters in London, subsidized by the Project, collects and analyzes reports on all locust movements and weather data, and keeps governments informed. An East Africa Locust Control Organization was recently established with FAO initiative, and efforts are being made to establish others in southwest Asia, North Africa, and the Near East.

The locust has temporarily disappeared as a plague. Why, nobody knows. But one thing is sure: it will return and vigilance cannot be relaxed.

Special Fund projects, numerous as they are, constitute only one of several U.N. approaches, and a fairly recent one, to the problems of agriculture in Egypt. Beginning its work in Egypt 20 years ago, FAO has had a profound influence on agriculture there. First came the FAO Regular Program, with its publications, statistics, conferences, training centers, and seminars. Then came technical assistance (e.g. for wheat and barley breeding, control of wheat rust and maize diseases, rice breeding, hybrid corn development, fisheries statistics, agricultural marketing, agricultural mechanization, nutrition, rural services and industries). In 1959 and after, Special Fund projects were added. More recently, help has come from the Freedom From Hunger Campaign and the World Food Program.

If Egypt has benefited disproportionately to other countries from FAO/Special Fund resources, it is only in a minor degree. Sudan has eight similar FAO/Special Fund projects, Syria four, and Peru eight, just to choose some examples at random. It is true, however, that FAO/Special Fund projects are concluded more easily with countries which possess some relevant institutions and technology, however rudimentary, and at least enough trained or semi-trained people to work with. They depend even more upon the interest of a government, its ability to draw up a suitable proposal, and its willingness to commit time, people, and money to carry it out. This is the case with Egypt.

Many Special Fund enterprises relating to agriculture, forestry, and fisheries would have been impossible had not their foundations been laid during previous years of FAO operations carried on under its Regular Program and with the assistance of EPTA. This is well illustrated by two Special Fund projects which I came across in Chile: the Institute for the Development of Forest Resources and Industries, and the Fisheries Development Institute. Both are located in Santiago.

Chile is blessed by nature with about 50 million acres of natural forests which protect the soil and supply local needs for construction, fuel and furniture. But Chile is also blessed by man and by accident with about 750,000 acres of Insignis pine which serves as the basis of a nascent but potentially large industrial wood industry. Towards the end of the last century a large Chilean landholder ordered a certain kind of pine seed from the United States and by mistake was sent seeds of the Insignis pine which promptly grew in Chile's soil and climate two or three times faster than in the United States or elsewhere. Today, from Concepcion southward you see seemingly endless man-planted stands of well-tended Insignis pine.

Nevertheless, before FAO began its help there in 1951 little was done to exploit the new forests or protect and modernize production in the old ones. Since then an FAO forestry mission has been continuously at work in Chile. One of the first accomplishments was the creation in 1952 of a Forestry School at the University of Chile in which FAO experts served for several years as professors. A number of fellows were also sent abroad for training. Today the Forestry School is well established, and for some years now has been turning out ten to fifteen graduate foresters each year. (There were only two trained foresters in the country in 1951.) In succeeding years the FAO mission occupied itself with forest legislation, improvement of forestry administration, the creation of a forest service, and forest management. It also provided assistance to the government and to private groups in the development of forest products industries and gave special assistance and equipment through an "Earthquake Mission" following the 1960 disaster. Finally, it drew up a national forest development policy which was adopted by the government. All of this, including the training of eleven fellows and the supply of thirty-nine different experts and equipment worth $400,000, preceded the establishment of the Forestry Institute in 1961 with Special Fund and FAO help.

This Institute is already well established and recognized as the competent authority in all matters relating to forests and forest industries. It has under way more than thirty different projects extending from silviculture through kiln drying of wood to board manufacture. Its director is a redoubtable Finn of exceptional competence named by FAO as project manager, Lars Hartman, a man who served many years in Chile as a forestry expert under FAO auspices during the 1950's. Its co-director is a Chilean. Seventeen of the professionals on the staff are foreign experts recruited by FAO; a larger number are Chileans. The Special Fund is contributing $1,268,800 for 5 years for FAO experts and equipment; the Chilean Government, $900,000. The Institute has responsibility for evaluating forest resources and improving their management and conservation, for advising on the development of new products and new industries, for training government and industrial personnel, for improving marketing and promoting demand, and for conducting applied research.

This is a tall order, and it is doubtful that Chile would have had the outlook, the policies, and the people to fill it if FAO, with EPTA's help, had not been at work for 10 years preparing the way for it. The Institute is doing well and prospects are good that it can carry on competently when U.N. support ends 2 years hence. One of its main activities has been the preparation of a 10-year plan for the development of the timber industry in the province of Arauco. The expenditure of $3 million to carry out the plan is expected to attract some $32 million in private capital investment. Already Chile is supplying most of its needs for pulp and paper, and has become an exporter, the first in Latin America. A large and thriving forest products industry is clearly in the making in Chile, an industry which may overtake in economic importance the declining copper industry.

The director and co-director of the new Fisheries Development Institute of Chile were elated the morning I drove with them from Santiago to visit some of their operations in Valparaiso. Moments before we left they received word that one of the experimental fishing crews had taken a ton of shrimps in new grounds. Laughing like boys, they planned to send boxes of the new shrimp, well iced, to a couple of leading doubters in the capital.

The Fisheries Institute, a joint product of the Government of Chile, the Special Fund, and FAO, began operations only in the fall of 1963 but, like the Forestry Institute, it has a wide background of FAO preparation.

In spite of 3000 miles of coastline whose adjacent waters teem with untold fishery wealth, fishing in Chile remained until recent years a small, untended enterprise of little commercial or industrial importance. (The same was true of fisheries in other countries in Latin America.) In 1952 FAO organized and instructed in Valparaiso a first Latin American Fisheries Training Center. Participating were thirty Chileans, among whom were Antonio Bories and Marcello Montt, two young men who very shortly went to Europe for a year's study on FAO fellowships and returned to found a Fisheries School at the Catholic University of Valparaiso. The school, starting with 20 students, now has 130. Mr. Bories is now director of the Fisheries Institute and was one of my companions on the morning ride to Valparaiso.

The 1952 Training Center was only the beginning of FAO fisheries help to Chile. During the next ten years FAO sent to that country seventeen specialists who studied and made recommendations on various aspects of fisheries development. Among them were J. P. d'Alarcao, a hardworking Spaniard, and Peter Molteno, a gentle-mannered South African, both first-class men in their fields. They made reports which are recognized as having laid the basis for Chile's fishing industry. Peter Molteno, now FAO project manager and co-director of the Fisheries Institute, was my second companion on my trip to Valparaiso, and d'Alarcao, with whom we joined up in nearby Viña del Mar, is now FAO's Regional Fisheries Officer for Latin America. Other Chileans who attended the 1952 Training Center or have since studied abroad with FAO fellowships now occupy important posts in fisheries administration, private fishery industries, and with FAO. There is a second Fisheries School now at Antofagasta.

Some of the results of U.N. stimulus to Chilean fishery initiative are dramatic. Six years ago several companies in Concepcion were going broke trying to make fish meal out of hake. Following FAO recommendations, and with government help, they moved their operations far north to Iquique, Arica and Antofagasta where their raw product is anchovies. There, their operations were so immediately successful and profitable that Chilean capital and foreign capital (from the United States, Germany, Denmark, Norway and South Africa) have been rushing into construction of new factories. At the beginning of 1964 there were already 25 large fish meal factories in the north operating 120 boats, and fish meal exports had increased from the insignificant to an estimated $10 million a year. Within 3 years it is expected that 50 to 60 factories (25 of these are already under construction) and 300 boats will be operating, and that fish meal exports will reach $60 million a year.

Meanwhile, as results of U.N. help, production, local consumption and exportation of salt and dried fish have increased sharply. Factories are going up which will can or freeze tuna, swordfish, and shrimp for export. And consumption of fresh fish in Santiago alone has increased by 40 per cent in the last 3 years.

All of this happened before the creation of the Fisheries Development Institute in the autumn of 1963, and incidentally it may be said that without 10 years of preparation with FAO/EPTA help, it is doubtful that the Institute could have been created. But it is now established, and it has a big job before it, for all that is past is prologue and Chile's fisheries have enormous potential. Nevertheless, fishing and fish processing and marketing are highly complex businesses. The new Institute, a permanent institution, is charged with solving the industry's problems and helping it to grow.

Perhaps the most significant thing about Chile's fisheries story is that it has its parallel in a number of other countries of Latin America, outstandingly in Peru.

I have mentioned in this chapter only 10 out of some 485 Special Fund projects — only 10 out of the 195 projects with which FAO is concerned. When one considers the whole range of projects there is no question that the Special Fund is one of the great operations of our time, conducted in such a way as to produce maximum effect in building institutions, training people, and attracting capital investment.

CHAPTER 4

HELPING CHILDREN TO MORE AND BETTER FOOD

THERE are probably tens of millions of people the world over who never heard of EPTA or the Special Fund or FAO but register recognition at the mention of UNICEF and associate it properly with the care and feeding of children. The U.N. International Children's Emergency Fund was one of the first creations of the fledgling United Nations. The General Assembly established it in December 1946, to help hungry and sick children in countries which had been devastated by war, and provided it with some starting money left over from the U.N. Relief and Rehabilitation Administration which had gone out of business a few months earlier. Continuing contributions were invited from governments and from private sources. UNICEF therefore went promptly to work and has been going strong and stronger ever since.

In the years since its creation as a temporary operation UNICEF has acquired permanent status (in 1953), has dropped "Emergency" and "International" from its title (it is now the U.N. Children's Fund although it retains the initials UNICEF), and has undergone several changes of emphasis and function. How can you care for the needs of children in a compartment separate from the needs of pregnant and nursing mothers, or separate from the family, the community and the nation? The answer is that you cannot. Logic has therefore led to a continuous expansion of the scope of UNICEF. Its focus has nevertheless been consistently on the needs of children.

If UNICEF had been confined to its original function of emergency feeding, clothing and disease control there would be no reason to take more than passing notice of it in a book devoted to what the United Nations is doing to increase the productivity of the world's lands, forests — and people. But over the years its functions have been enlarged, with the result that it has entered fields cultivated by FAO and other members of the U.N. family, making possible and necessary close cooperation in joint projects.

In 1950 the U.N. General Assembly authorized UNICEF to advance from emergency relief to continuing child care programs, chiefly in the underdeveloped countries. UNICEF immediately increased its attention to pregnant and nursing mothers, the training of midwives, and the equipment of maternal and child health centers, all of which are within the competence of the World Health Organization (WHO). It also extended its interest in milk conservation, which is within the scope of FAO. In 1958 UNICEF entered the fields of applied nutrition and the development and promotion of high protein food where both WHO and FAO were working. Interest in nutrition led to increased concern for nutrition education, administration, teacher training, and the establishment of teacher training institutions, all of which to some degree are within the competence, not only of WHO and FAO, but also of UNESCO (U.N. Educational Scientific and Cultural Organization). In 1961, with the concurrence of the other U.N. agencies which had studied the matter, UNICEF broadened its scope still further to include all the major needs of children and youth, and increased its support for programs in education, vocational training, home economics, and broad social services. Thus it ventured into areas of interest not only to FAO, UNESCO and WHO, but also to the U.N. Bureau of Economic and Social Affairs and the International Labour Organization (ILO). Finally, UNICEF shifted, as did the other members of the U.N. family, from assistance to individual unrelated projects to increased emphasis upon long-range plans and programs to meet the needs of children and youth — towards the creation of permanent institutions and practices within the context of a national plan rather than doing a little here and there.*

* UNICEF projects and FAO nutrition work involve activities which are described by technical terms that are not familar to the layman. Here, therefore, are some descriptions that may be useful:

Milk conservation involves breeding and husbandry of dairy animals; feed production, pastures and animal nutrition; animal health and disease

To those who do not know how UNICEF works as a member of the U.N. family this looks like a situation tailor-made for confusion, duplication, contention and waste. Actually, although there have been differences between the headquarters of several organizations over who should pay for what, there has been remarkably little confusion and duplication in the field programs. Nevertheless, any logical person is likely to ask "What on earth does UNICEF have that other members of the family, which collectively cover its field, do not have?"

It has several things. First and most important, it has popular appeal, and because it has appeal it has money over and above what other agencies can attract. It is simply a fact of life that governments and people the world over dig deeper into their pockets to help children and mothers. Second, UNICEF money, unlike that of most other U.N. agencies, can be spent on supplies: special foods, medicines, hospital and laboratory equipment, and the like. Third,

---

control; milk production and collection; milk and dairy products processing plants and their operation and management; the storage, handling, distribution and marketing of milk products and their use in human consumption, especially by the most vulnerable groups in a population; and price policies, incentives and organization.

Applied nutrition covers a wide range of activities to improve the diets of pregnant or nursing mothers, including school and community feeding, family feeding and sanitation, training in nutrition and development of national nutritional surveys and nutritional services. Projects emphasize increased production, conservation, processing, storage and use of high protein and protective foods, including not only milk but meats and fish, grain legumes, vegetables and fruits, and poultry. They include school and community gardening and similar activities.

High protein food projects concern the development of new foods high in protein produced from local materials. Some of the foods being given attention are special formulas for baby foods and foods for young children, fish flour and other fish products, legume products and other food combinations making use of specially processed meat, eggs and other dairy products. Projects are concerned with the production, pilot processing, introduction and promotion of these foods.

Home economics projects involve instruction and training in child care, sanitation, and the feeding of the younger members of the family and their proper rearing and training. One important approach is through women's clubs and training of young women in the sciences and crafts essential for motherhood and home-making.

UNICEF has a professional focus which is a net addition to the work of the other U.N. agencies: without it, the other agencies certainly would not and could not pay as much attention to the special needs of mothers and young children. The UNICEF approach penetrates other agencies, gets attention, and the U.N. family cooperates to carry out projects.

UNICEF has a lean and efficient organization and for 18 years had as executive director a remarkable man, the late Maurice Pate, who made and kept it so. In addition to New York headquarters, UNICEF in March 1965 maintained six regional offices and twenty-six field offices supervising operations in single countries or groups of countries. Its total staff in New York and in the field, including clerical staff, numbered 754, of which 188 were U.N. professionals, 330 were local professionals paid by UNICEF, and 236 were local staff paid by governments.

UNICEF is in its very essence a U.N. family affair. Its projects require advice and supervision in the field by technical experts. And who supplies these field experts? Why, one or more of the members of the U.N. family most competent to do so — FAO, WHO, UNESCO, or some other, depending upon the nature of the work. And who pays for these field experts? This varies and is frequently a sore point. WHO usually pays for its own. Most of the other agencies usually try to get them financed through EPTA, and when they cannot do so they either dig into their own budgets or, as in the case of FAO, UNICEF foots much of the bill. In general, all of the agencies, including FAO, pay for their central headquarters and regional services to UNICEF programs.

Relying upon other members of the U.N. family for technical assistance in the field, UNICEF seeks their help beforehand in preparing projects and working out plans of operation with governments. The Executive Board of UNICEF declines to consider any project until it has been approved by the technical U.N. agency or agencies concerned. Thus almost all UNICEF operations are co-operative from the beginning to end. In the typical program the original idea, the initiative, and the supplies and equipment, are furnished by UNICEF; the government concerned asks for and administers the project, and the field experts and technical back-stopping by headquarters are furnished by the U.N. agencies. It is not at all uncommon, however, for the idea and the initiative to originate with the agencies and to be adopted by UNICEF. Although it sounds complicated, it works well.

The World Health Organization (WHO), concerned as it is with health services and disease control, is the largest collaborator with UNICEF. FAO, with special technical competence in milk production and conservation, applied nutrition, nutrition education and training, the development of high protein foods, and home economics is the second largest. In September 1963 there were 122 joint FAO/UNICEF projects in operation, and another two dozen worked out with governments awaiting approval by the UNICEF Executive Board. In addition, FAO is engaged jointly with WHO in another twenty-six UNICEF projects, with UNESCO in another nine, and with the U.N. Bureau of Social Affairs in another two. In quite a number of these, three and sometimes four agencies are contributing technical assistance to the same program. For example, a UNICEF program of applied nutrition education and training in Peru involves technical assistance from FAO, UNESCO, and WHO.

During the last 7 years governments have grown increasingly concerned with nutrition and nutrition education, and annual contributions to UNICEF have risen substantially. FAO also has steadily increased its own budgeted funds for nutrition work since 1958 and, with EPTA-financed experts, increased its nutrition activities in the field.

Much of the increase in UNICEF activity since 1958 has involved FAO. In 1958, UNICEF allocations for FAO-guided projects were $4.5 million. By 1962, UNICEF allocations for FAO-guided projects had risen to $26.7 million and in 1964 to $30 million. This sixfold increase has obviously transformed FAO/UNICEF operations from a minor to a major activity. UNICEF initiative and funds have greatly enriched FAO operations, and FAO technical competence has been not only helpful but necessary to UNICEF's effectiveness.

There is very little if any difference between FAO nutrition projects and FAO/UNICEF projects. Both organizations, with a minimum of confusion and no duplication, are operating in the same field, and the field is to say the least big enough to require their joint efforts. It is shocking that in our so-called modern age there are many countries where more than half the deaths are of children under 5 years of age. It is even more shocking that of those deaths, a large proportion are the result of malnutrition. Moreover, there are tens of millions of undernourished children who survive childhood but are handicapped throughout their lives by irreparable early damage to their nervous systems, vital organs and mental powers. This is not only a massive tragedy in itself but obstructs efforts to improve the situation. Nutritional services, education, and training are not peripheral "do-goodism". They are of the essence of economic and social advancement.

As far as I have been able to learn, there is no significant criticism of the way FAO/UNICEF joint projects are conducted in the field nor doubts about their importance. Nearly everybody agrees that FAO/UNICEF collaboration is necessary and fruitful. It is unfortunate, therefore, that there should be discord between these two members of the U.N. family over the perennial question of who pays for what.

Although it has independent funds, UNICEF is not an independent agency. Its executive director is appointed by the U.N. Secretary-General. Its Governing Executive Board, which consists of the representatives of thirty countries, is appointed by the Economic and Social Council. And its staff is part of the U.N. Secretariat in New York. UNICEF officially holds that members of the U.N. family, such as FAO, which have formal responsibility for supplying technical experts for UNICEF programs, should find the means to finance them, either through EPTA or out of their own budgets, and that it is in principle wrong to do otherwise. In earlier years, FAO held that administrative and operational costs of a joint project should be borne by the organization which initiated it. These two official positions set the stage for contention. However, in 1960 the Director General of FAO and the Executive Director of UNICEF agreed that in principle FAO should provide the technical experts needed for joint projects, and presumably find the financing for them, but that until FAO could find a satisfactory way of doing this, UNICEF would continue to "bridge the gap" by paying for such experts as could not be financed by EPTA. FAO has never found a satisfactory way: the FAO Conference has been unwilling to provide the funds.

In recent years, with UNICEF funds and FAO/UNICEF projects increasing, and with EPTA unable to finance all the FAO experts needed for them, UNICEF has been obliged to make steadily increasing allocations to FAO to enable it to provide technical experts for joint projects — from $238,000 in 1960 to $1,413,640 in 1963. Nevertheless, UNICEF has protested year after year that this is not just, and that FAO should make provision in its own budget for technical assistance to FAO/UNICEF projects. In 1963, roughly one-half of FAO technical assistance to joint FAO/UNICEF projects was financed by UNICEF. The FAO Conference in November 1963 expressed appreciation for UNICEF's action in "bridging the gap" and the hope that it would continue to do so. Clearly there has been no solution.

The differences between FAO and UNICEF are illustrated by an interchange that occurred during the FAO Conference in November 1963. The delegate from India, in agreeing with the UNICEF position that FAO should bear the cost of technical assistance for joint projects, remarked that "the relationship (between FAO and UNICEF) is like that between two members of a family or husband and wife where one agency provides the equipment and material and the other executes and supervises the project". Later in the debate the delegate from the United Kingdom had this to say: "I sympathize too with the analogy drawn by the delegate from India as to the partnership being that as between the husband and wife, but I am sure he will forgive me if I say we all know there are many marriages in which one partner incurs expenditure which the other partner finds it difficult to meet."

Incidentally, the same difficulties prevailed in relations between UNICEF and WHO for years, until the World Health Assembly agreed in 1958 to finance its own technical assistance to UNICEF projects.

Another but related problem disturbs relations between FAO and UNICEF. The increasing number of joint projects in recent years has meant a proportionate increase in FAO headquarters costs for recruiting experts and supervising their activities. And although it has been agreed that FAO headquarters costs for joint programs shall be borne by FAO, the FAO Conference has been reluctant to provide enough funds for the purpose. In November 1963, FAO's Director General, Dr. B. R. Sen, proposed to the FAO Conference a budget item of $650,000 for headquarters and regional staff devoted to planning and supervising FAO/UNICEF work. (He did not ask for money for FAO technical assistance to field projects.) The request seemed reasonable, especially inasmuch as the Director General also proposed, and the Conference approved, expansion of nutrition work as one of the four major fields to be given increased emphasis in the FAO program during 1964 and 1965. Nevertheless, Dr. Sen's budget item ran into heavy opposition. Many governments were of the opinion that UNICEF should pay not only for FAO field costs in joint programs, but regional and headquarters costs as well. In the end the Conference approved the Director General's budget figure "within the limits of funds available". However, the "funds available" are not likely to be more than half the amount requested for 1964–5, far from enough to provide for effective back-stopping of FAO/UNICEF projects.

The debate on FAO/UNICEF relations revealed that while there is a U.N. family, the family spirit does not necessarily pervade in all relations at all times. Representatives of a number of governments spoke condescendingly of "their" (FAO/UNICEF) projects as contrasted with "our" (FAO) projects. Others said that if UNICEF was a fund it should act like a fund and distribute its money in lump sums to the agencies. They were reminded emphatically by Mrs. Zena Harmon, Chairman of UNICEF's Executive Board, that UNICEF was not just a fund but a U.N. organization created to do a job.

The root of the trouble is clear. Representatives of a number of countries on the Executive Board of UNICEF take the position at UNICEF Board meetings that FAO should bear the cost of its own technical assistance to UNICEF programs, plus headquarters costs, while representatives of the *same* governments maintain at the FAO Conference that those costs should be borne by UNICEF and decline to vote FAO budget support for them. It is all rather absurd, since the same amount of money must come from almost the *same* governments in any case. There is no difficulty here that could not be solved by clear thinking and consistent action by the governments which control and support both organizations.

This is a family wrangle and, although it gives continuing headaches to those who direct the operations of both organizations, it is not of great significance. The important thing is that field collaboration continues harmoniously and fruitfully.

All FAO/UNICEF projects, whether milk conservation, or home economics, or high protein food development, are concerned with nutrition, but in spite of all efforts, adequate nourishment for all people is likely to be very long deferred on this earth. For malnutrition, if not rooted in poverty and ignorance, grows out of tradition, habit, preference, and sloth. The principal cures for it are substantial incomes, general education, and changed community outlooks.

Forty years ago there was widespread malnutrition in the rural areas of the United States. Hundreds of thousands of country people were afflicted with pellagra, rickets and other diseases because of a winter diet of fatback and corn pone. Secretary of State Dean Rusk once described conditions such as these which existed in the Georgia of his childhood. And some of the most vivid recollections of my own youth in Texas are of my Uncle Kay, who was a progressive farmer, striding up and down the gallery that circled his farmhouse, raging against the practices of his farmer neighbors. Unlike him, they grew only cash crops, refused to keep a cow, or raise hogs or cattle for slaughtering, and were too lazy to plant or tend gardens. They cured no meat for the winter, preserved no vegetables or fruits as his wife did. When they had spent the paltry cash received from the sale of cotton and corn, they were reduced to the inevitable diet of fat, salt pork and corn bread, and their children sickened and frequently died. There is of course infinitely less of this in the United States today, but more than one might suspect in remote areas. Most of it was cured in recent decades by a political New Deal, vast and expensive agricultural extension services with agriculture and home economics agents in each county, higher prices for agricultural products sustained by costly Federal price supports, farm credit, rural electrification, improved roads, more and better schools, the radio, and finally by mechanization of agriculture. Not a bad prescription, if a nation can afford it!

But this is out of the question in poor countries with average incomes of less than $100 a year, high illiteracy, skeleton government services, and poor communications. Leaders in those countries know that the basic cure for malnutrition lies in development all across the board, and that is what they are trying to accomplish. But improvement comes slowly. Meanwhile, short of full-scale national prosperity, there are ways of reducing the rate of infant mortality caused by malnutrition, for spreading knowledge about diet, and for spreading improved food growing and eating habits. Leaders of the underdeveloped countries, painfully aware of the obvious blight of malnutrition and its drag on general improvement, have been increasingly eager to try all short-cuts to improved nutrition, and the governments of advanced countries, the U.N. agencies, and private foundations and welfare organizations the world over, are eager to help.

Not long ago in Ibadan, second city of Nigeria, I stood before a huge city map which covered almost the entire wall of the room in a hospital. Ibadan is not far from the capital, a flourishing commercial center, the home of a first-rate university. The map had a pin stuck in it for each case of the dreadful kwashiorkor disease reported in the last several years. One could scarcely see the map for the pins: there were thousands. Kwashiorkor is the most malignant of the many children's afflictions directly caused by a shortage of proteins and amino-acids in their diets. Anyone who sees a ward full of small children suffering from kwashiorkor never forgets it. The most painful thing about the sight is the knowledge that it could have been prevented by even rudimentary attention to diet, even with foods locally available. It can be cured easily with scientific care and feeding in well-equipped hospitals. But how many people have access to such hospitals? Kwashiorkor is widely prevalent in Africa, parts of Asia, and some countries of Latin America. But this is only one consequence of malnutrition. Others are pellagra, beri-beri, rickets, polyneuritis, sores, and the degrading weakness and lassitude that afflicts young and old alike. No government that aspires to improve the conditions of its people can ignore the problem of malnutrition, extremely difficult though it is to solve.

Nutritionists do not yet know all about nutrition, but they know a great deal, and their knowledge is increasing. They have learned that the proteins that come from milk, meat, fish, and certain beans, nuts and seeds, are essential to health. They are aware of the importance of the acids and vitamins in fresh vegetables. Their problem is to try to get people to produce these foods, eat them, and feed them to their children. They approach the problem at all levels from the national government administration down to the classroom.

Of basic importance is a national government administration concerned with the problem and staffed by people with nutrition knowledge and background. A good extension service is also of the essence, and there must be knowledgeable, trained people to man it. Finally, there must be a horde of trained village workers. The U.N. family has therefore concentrated heavily on creating nutrition training centers, schools for nutrition teachers, fellowships for training nutrition workers, and direct advice and assistance to governments in carrying on nutrition programs. For education is the key, and the first step is training teachers and administrators, and training the teachers of those who instruct the village workers. But the ultimate hope lies in training the young. There is also, therefore, heavy accent in U.N. projects on pilot and demonstration feeding programs in the schools, and on school gardening programs where young people receive practical experience in agriculture, horticulture, livestock feeding, the principles of food marketing and distribution, and food technology.

Most countries have actual or potential sources of vital proteins and acids which are not used in local diets because they are not palatable without processing. Considerable U.N. effort therefore goes into isolating the essential food elements in these products, introducing them into foods that are palatable, and promoting their consumption. For example, in Indonesia, a spray-dried extract from soybean and sesame is now commercially produced and widely accepted by the people. In Brazil a new protein-rich product based on soybeans is being introduced into the market with the support of the government. A new peanut flour high in protein is being mixed with millet flour in Senegal and has been successfully introduced into the market. In Nigeria a similar peanut flour mixed with dried skimmed milk is being promoted widely by the government. The production of a palatable fish flour, high in protein value, is being fostered in FAO/UNICEF projects in Morocco, Peru and Chile, and elsewhere. Efforts are being made in many countries to develop tasty foods using the desired elements of oil seeds such as sesame, sunflower, and coconut, and to promote their consumption.

Some of the most successful nutrition efforts of FAO and UNICEF have been made in India. A pilot project of considerable size was first undertaken in 1959 in the State of Orissa. In an area covering 240 villages three FAO experts helped the government carry on an extensive program of applied nutrition which included demonstration, training, school gardening and work with women's clubs. This was followed by similar pilot projects in the States of Andhra Pradesh, Madras and Uttar Pradesh. These successful experiments led the Government of India to draw up a master plan for an applied nutrition program which is expected eventually to cover the whole country, a program to be carried out with the help of FAO, UNICEF and WHO. Its major aim is to train specialists in all aspects of nutrition work, including methods of working in the rural villages. Already eight full-time FAO experts are helping in this program, and others contribute part of their time.

Important work is also being done by FAO and UNICEF in Africa. For instance, in Sierra Leone training centers are being set up in each province to train the trainers of village workers in home improvement and family nutrition. In Basutoland FAO, UNICEF and WHO are together carrying on an extensive program of nutrition, administration and training. Similar work is being done in Senegal and many other African countries. Other examples of FAO/UNICEF collaboration run into the hundreds.

D

CHAPTER 5

USING FOOD AS A DEVELOPMENT TOOL

THE youngest member of the U.N. family of organizations concerned with food and agriculture is only 2 years old and whether it is to survive, and in what form, will not be determined until it is three. Nevertheless, the World Food Program (WFP) as of mid-1964 is a vigorous and flourishing youngster with bright hopes not only for survival but for a significant and productive life. In effect it is a highly promising extension of the work of the U.N. and FAO.

Unknown to the public, WFP is both more and less than its name suggests. It operates in many parts of the world but it is not a program in the usual sense of the word. Rather, like UNICEF, it is a fund, even though a very special kind of fund, administered by an operating agency. Certainly at its present stage it cannot aim to feed the world. Its resources for an experimental 3-year run consist of an authorized $100 million, chiefly in commodities, but they also include cash (hopefully one-third of the total) and services (shipping and insurance). All this is pledged by governments, half of it by the United States. Most of the commodities contributed are considered as surplus by the donor countries. The main purpose of WFP is to use surplus food directly as capital to promote economic and social progress in less developed countries, but its resources are also used to help governments carry on feeding programs in special circumstances, and for disaster relief.

Of all the ironies that affront common and moral sense the existence of costly, troublesome food surpluses and unused production capacity in some countries alongside of hunger and malnutrition in other ranks near the top of the list. In countries where they are produced, food surpluses are a weight on the conscience, a burden on the taxpayer, and a constant headache to the government. In countries without enough food, surpluses in others are the focus of envy and discontent. And yet, it is difficult for nations with the best will in the world to bring surpluses together with needs in ways that are wholly satisfactory.

No country, no people on earth, is happy or willing to be dependent indefinitely upon the charity and caprice of others for the primary necessity of life. Basic food, if nothing else, they want to be able to produce or buy. Moreover, unless precautions are taken and limits observed, bulk give-away of food, other than in emergencies and for special uses, disrupts normal commercial markets or prevents their expansion, generates discord in international relations, and discourages local food production. These facts are accepted by food surplus and food deficit countries alike. However, after World War II the relentless pressures of surplus and need generated ferment, study, and experimentation which have widened enormously the scope for constructive international use of surplus food without damaging side effects.

To the United States, the chief producer of surplus food, is due most of the credit both for most of the ideas and the action as far as bulk food transfers are concerned. The sale of food surpluses to a needy country with payment in its inconvertible local currency, and with most of the currency then being either frozen or loaned or granted back to the country for financing the local costs of reconstruction or economic development projects, was a feature of the Marshall Plan for European recovery. This conception was embodied in 1954 in Title I of the well-known U.S. Public Law 480 under which the United States has supplied more than $12 billion of surplus agricultural commodities to underdeveloped countries. This food supply on easy terms has allowed the countries to spend their meager supplies of foreign exchange for machinery and other capital goods for development rather than for imported food, and at the same time it has provided them with funds arising from local sale of the food to finance some of the local costs of development. By their very nature these transactions have not added to inflationary pressures in the developing countries. Being "sales", they do not offend the pride of the buyers. And they have been conducted in such a way that their effects upon normal commercial trade have been minimal. Without any question, they constitute one of the great innovations of our times and have done untold good.

The United States has also given needy countries huge amounts of surplus food for relief in cases of crop failures and other disasters, and for feeding programs undertaken and supervised by U.S. welfare agencies. And it has pioneered in grants of food for partial direct payment of labor costs of development projects such as the building of roads, dams, and irrigation works.* All of this, it should perhaps be emphasized, has been done by the United States in bilateral arrangements. Canada, Australia and New Zealand have also helped other countries by selling them surplus food at less than commercial market prices.

Notwithstanding the urges and desires of FAO Directors General, the role of the United Nations in the use of surpluses has been restricted by FAO's governing Conference to serving up information on surpluses and needs, giving advice, prodding publicly and incessantly, and formulating rules and procedures to reduce or eliminate damaging side effects on commercial trade. It has been a helpful and important role, but its limitations have not been easy for the Director General and the Secretariat of FAO to bear. With sensibilities rubbed raw by daily, abrasive contract with the realities of surpluses coexisting with unfilled need, the first Director General of FAO, Lord John Boyd Orr, labored mightily but in vain for four years to bring about the creation of a World Food Board with wide powers to stabilize prices, hold and manage reserve stocks, and finance the movement of food from surplus to deficit countries. His successor, Mr. Norris Dodd, tried in 1953 with equal lack of success to secure backing for an international emergency food reserve. These efforts have been described in detail elsewhere† and need not be elaborated upon here. The heat was turned down for international action after 1954 when the United States launched its

* Credit for originating and popularizing the idea belongs to a man who at the time was in charge of economics work in FAO — Mordecai Ezekiel.

† Gove Hambidge, *The Story of FAO*, Van Nostrand, New York, London and Toronto, 1955.

vast, bilateral surplus use programs under Public Law 480, with several other countries following suit. In 1957 the FAO Conference recommended international cooperation to establish national food reserves and although this was endorsed by the U.N. Economic and Social Council, only a few countries have shown any interest, much less acted. Looking back on these earlier efforts, FAO's present Director General, Dr. B. R. Sen, concluded in 1961 that "the main reason for lack of progress appears to have been the reluctance of governments to undertake measures which might weaken their national initiative and national powers of control".

This in effect was the situation when in 1960 the United States, reversing a position it had long and firmly held, introduced into the U.N. General Assembly a "Resolution on Provision of Food Surpluses to Food Deficit Peoples through the United Nations System". Passed by the General Assembly on 27 October 1960, the Resolution called upon FAO to undertake, among other things, a study of "additional arrangements, including multilateral arrangements under the auspices of the Food and Agriculture Organization, having as their objective the mobilization of available surplus foodstuffs and their distribution in areas of greatest need, particularly in the economically less developed countries".

FAO's Director General Sen may have been surprised by this sudden turn of events, but not too much to catch the ball running, and it looks as though he may have made a record for speed. With the approval of the FAO Council he promptly appointed five renowned independent experts to advise him. Within less than 6 months the experts had submitted their findings to him; Dr. Sen had prepared a report and recommendations for action taking account of the views of the experts; and the report and recommendations had been thoroughly threshed by a high-powered intergovernmental advisory committee which met in Rome in April 1961. It was at this meeting that the U.S. representative, Food for Peace Director George McGovern, surprised and delighted all present, and gave the whole exercise substance, by proposing a $100 million fund in cash and commodities, pledging the United States to contribute at least 40 per cent of it. The author of this book happened to be an unofficial advisor to Mr. McGovern at the meeting. The Food for Peace Director had cabled home for permission to make the proposal and had performed the miracle of getting an official decision from Washington over a weekend in springtime. It is not known whether certain officials in the U.S. State Department and the Department of Agriculture ever really forgave him for their lost weekend.

Be that as it may, Dr. Sen's report and recommendations, enriched by the U.S. suggestions and pledge, found prompt favor, after a few modifications, with the U.N. Secretary-General, the U.N. Economic and Social Council, the FAO Council and Conference, and the U.N. General Assembly. Thus, within a year after the United Nations had ordered a study the way was open for a joint U.N./FAO $100 million 3-year experimental World Food Program. Its seat is at FAO headquarters in Rome; its Executive Director is appointed jointly by FAO's Director General and the U.N. Secretary-General; and its governing body is an intergovernmental committee consisting of representatives of twenty-four nations, half named by the United Nations and half by FAO. A. H. Boerma, formerly an Assistant Director General of FAO, was named Executive Director. At a pledging conference in September 1962, thirty-three governments committed themselves to $86 million. The WFP was in business. As of 1 March 1964, sixty-four governments had pledged $91 million as follows: commodities $65.9 million; cash $19.3 million; insurance and shipping services $5.5 million.

A potential embarrassment to operations is the shortage of cash in the fund. There is scarcely a direct food-use that does not require a certain amount of cash to make it effective: money to buy equipment, accessory supplies and storage facilities. Moreover, cash is required for shipping, insurance, superintendence, and administration. Those who guide the destinies of WFP figure that the right proportion of cash to food is one dollar in cash to two in food, but the proportion in the WFP fund has never been more than one to three. Repeated exhortations have brought a modest increase in the cash contributions, but they are still one-third short of the target.

The reader will naturally wonder why the United States suddenly switched position and encouraged the U.N. family to begin to assume some responsibility for using surplus food, including a small part of its own, in aid projects. There are several reasons and they are significant.

Perhaps the most important reason was that in the late 1950's pressure of "have not" countries in the United Nations for greater help from the "haves" to relieve hunger and poverty and step up the pace of economic development rose toward a danger point. FAO's worldwide Freedom from Hunger Campaign,* conceived by Dr. Sen, unveiled before ECOSOC in 1958, approved by the FAO Conference in 1959, and launched in 1960 was both a response to the pressure and a goad to greater action. The U.N. Resolution of 27 October 1960, which ordered the study resulting in WFP, began by approving and endorsing FAO's Freedom from Hunger Campaign. And the General Assembly which passed that resolution launched a month later the U.N. Development Decade. In this climate it became necessary to do everything conceivable to use surplus food to feed the hungry and promote development.

For its part the United States had found that its pioneering, experimental food grants to countries for direct use as a development tool — for part payment of labor costs on construction projects — had not been entirely satisfactory. The main surplus foods it had to offer and whose supply was certain were wheat and corn. Other items in its surplus larder, especially butter, soybean oil, and protein foods such as dried milk and cheese, fluctuated in quantity and frequently disappeared from the larder altogether. It was difficult therefore, if not impossible, to provide a balanced diet to workers on construction projects. Moreover, workers not infrequently rejected food as payment for their labor, considering it an infraction of their dignity. They preferred cash, and the food had to be sold to pay wages in cash. Experience with this kind of operation was limited. Thus the idea grew among officials concerned in the United States that it might be just as well for U.N. agencies, calling on experts from all over the world, to experiment with the use of food as a development tool rather than carry on the difficult business all alone.

---

* For a full account of the Freedom from Hunger Campaign, see Chapter 5 of Part IV.

Another advantage was even clearer. Many countries which could supply food for aid purposes, especially the protein foods so greatly needed — fish products, cheese, beans, and the like — were not doing so. One of the deterrents for the smaller countries was no doubt the prohibitive cost of operating singly a program of food aid based on their own occasional surpluses. United Nations operations might elicit greater cooperation from those countries and provide a wider variety of foods, and more cash and services to go with it.

Notwithstanding the good done in the world by its enormous food transfers under bilateral arrangements, the United States has been the target of criticism, sometimes loud, sometimes muted, that its "surplus disposal" programs disrupt the normal commercial trade of other countries. The criticism was especially vehement in the middle 1950's when the United States was new in the surplus disposal business. That it has declined is due to FAO initiative and the willingness of the United States and other surplus-producing countries to cooperate in procedures to reduce friction. Aware both of the great advantages and dangers of providing needy countries with food at cut-rates or easy terms, FAO's permanent Intergovernmental Committee on Commodity Problems in 1954 drew up a Code of Principles of Surplus Disposal and established in Washington a continuing Subcommittee on Surplus Disposal which has ever since ridden herd on international surplus transactions. Complaints may be lodged with the Subcommittee and the result is that more often than not large deals are submitted by exporting countries to the governments of their competitors for discussion and approval before they are closed. The results have been remarkably good. Most countries concerned, including the United States, adhere to the Principles, follow the Guiding Lines, and cooperate closely with the Subcommittee. As a result complaints have greatly diminished. Nevertheless, some exporting countries and some private traders maintain a low rumble of discontent. This is another reason why the United States has become willing to share with the United Nations its responsibility for international aid use of its abundance. If there is a rap to be taken, let the United Nations share that too!

The final and immediate reason for reversal of the U.S. position was domestic and political in the U.S. election year of 1960. For years the Democrats, notably Hubert Humphrey, then Senator and now Vice-President, had been winning friends and influencing growing numbers of people with the slogan "Food For Peace", meaning an even greater use of U.S. agricultural surpluses to meet world need. In 1960 President Eisenhower unexpectedly appropriated the slogan and "Food For Peace" became bipartisan. One result was the U.S. initiative in the United Nations which later, under President Kennedy, materialized in the form of a concrete U.S. proposal for an experimental World Food Program.

If there was any question whether there was much fertile ground left for WFP to cultivate between the fields already tilled by national governments and U.N. agencies, it has already been answered in less than two years of WFP operations. By the middle of June 1964 WFP had received 166 requests from 56 governments in Asia, Africa and Latin America, and even Europe, for food help in projects of economic and social development, and it had committed $31 million for 53 of these projects in 32 countries. Moreover, it had spent or committed $9.1 million to help victims of catastrophes in 12 countries. Dozens of other requests were in various stages of processing leading toward approval.

Although WFP food help is by no means limited to agricultural development, two-thirds of the requests and most of the projects approved thus far are of that nature, involving land settlement and livestock improvement.

In Sudan, 50,000 people, whose land in the Wadi Haifa district is to be covered with 30 feet of Nile water as Egypt's new Aswan High Dam is completed, are being moved 800 miles and resettled in Kashm-el-Girba. WFP is supplying over 5000 tons of food to sustain the settlers on their long trek and tide them over until their new land can sustain them. The Sudanese Government is furnishing agricultural tools and other needed equipment.

In a like manner WFP is helping the Government of Ghana resettle in 52 new villages 80,000 people displaced by waters which are to rise behind the new Volta River dam. WFP food is used to pay part of the wages of 2000 workers engaged in the construction of 10,000 houses, roads, draining systems and other public works. The resettlement project aims also at organizing cooperatives, diversifying crops and mechanizing farming, all of which is expected to change the existing pattern of subsistence farming.

Syria, Egypt, and in fact nearly all the countries of the Middle East and North Africa are hindered in their efforts to get ahead by the habits of the Bedouin, nomads whose tattered and patched black hair tents pitched in the most improbable places are such a familiar sight to a traveller in those lands. The Bedouin live as have their forbears for thousands of years, poor and illiterate, following uncertain rainfall with their herds of scrawny sheep. Their children who survive hunger and disease have no chance for an education which might allow them to improve their lot, and so the pattern continues generation after generation. Their sheep and goats descend upon newly discovered patches of vegetation, eat everything in sight and prevent the land from acquiring a sustained and respectable covering.

Unaided, there is no possibility of controlled grazing by the Bedouin, or range improvement or fattening animals for market, or building food reserves for man and beast for use during droughts. Governments are therefore trying to break the cycle of poverty-breeding-poverty by extraordinary assistance during a period of transition from wandering to settled farming. This means instruction and help in house building, well-digging, ground water management, dry farming and controlled grazing. It also means building and maintaining schools and health services. And most importantly, it means building food reserves and providing food for human beings and their animals during a transition period. Obviously, WFP food can play a significant role here as part of larger government programs of nomad settlement, and it is doing so under sizeable WFP arrangements with Syria, Egypt, and Jordan. Similar help to Saudi Arabia and other countries is under consideration. In these schemes part of the food is sold to the Bedouin at low prices on credit, repayments being used to build up a revolving emergency food fund.

A visit with a Bedouin family in the northwest coastal region of Egypt was for me an unforgettable experience. The ragged black tent looked weary to death of travelling, but nevertheless resignedly expectant of move on a moment's notice. Adjacent was the beginning of a rock house which looked as though it had been beginning for a long time, and there was a shallow well dug with the encouragement of the government. But there was no cultivation. Over a rise of land 200 yards behind the tent fourteen meager sheep watched by two children were chewing on sparse tufts of brown grass. Inside the tent, all was as neat and clean as it could be considering that it was pitched on bare caked earth, housed three generations, and was accessible to animals. And I found there pride, friendliness, and hospitality. Doubtless the whole establishment would shortly move on to greener fields, but it would return. And perhaps the following year, with house completed (but not yet lived in), with farming started, with food assured, the family would not move at all. They would probably buy a transistor radio and the children would go to the new school.

In Bolivia and Tanganyika where unemployed farm workers have flocked to the towns and cities, creating there social and political problems of a most serious nature, the governments are encouraging resettlement on hitherto uncultivated land. WFP food is helping to grub-stake the settlers until their new farms are in production. Reforestation of degraded forest lands is being undertaken by the governments in Turkey, Jamaica, and Morocco, and WFP food is being used for partial payment of workers. And so it goes: land settlement and reclamation, watershed management and animal husbandry are involved in the majority of WFP early undertakings.

The various U.N. family studies and resolutions which form the "Constitution" of the World Food Program clearly authorized the use of WFP food not only for economic and social development but also for direct feeding of the hungry and undernourished. This confronted the governing body of WFP and its Executive Director with a dilemma. With only a 3-year experimental program and limited resources, what would be gained if a substantial part were used to tackle unlimited hunger and malnutrition simply by distributing food? UNICEF had in the previous 15 years learned that this was an endless road with few permanent effects and had switched emphasis to feeding as an accessory to nutrition education and training. Should not WFP profit from UNICEF experience?

The answer was yes. In its experimental stage WFP is for the most part responding to government feeding requests only when feeding is part of an institutional effort leading to some kind of lasting effect. For example, Mauritania, short of educated or trained people, is making extraordinary efforts to expand boarding facilities at secondary and vocational schools and thereby attract increased and more regular attendance. WFP is helping to feed the boarders. Likewise, in Togo and Chad WFP food is being used by governments to attract greater school attendance by providing a midday meal. And in Bolivia, where the government is making a great effort in ten rural colleges to train more desperately needed rural teachers, WFP is providing food for the college boarders in amounts which have made possible a large increase in enrollment.

Among those who direct WFP and oversee its operations there is unease over the small number of requests for help in industrial development, but this is doubtless because WFP is not well known except in Ministries of Agriculture, and also because the economies of the underdeveloped countries are overwhelmingly agricultural. However, WFP maize is helping to expand a mechanized poultry feed factory in India, and in Turkey WFP food is proposed for use in extending and improving a number of industrial undertakings.

If requests for help in industrial projects have been smaller than expected, calls for emergency relief have perhaps been greater than foreseen and have obliged WFP management to limit disaster relief to 25 per cent of its experimental 3-year fund. Hardly had WFP opened its doors than a series of emergencies began to require its attention:

September 1962	earthquake in Iran
October 1962	hurricane in Thailand
November 1962	refugee movements in Algeria

January 1963	refugee swarms from Ruanda to Tanganyika
January 1963	floods in Morocco
April 1963	volcanic eruption in Bali
April 1963	floods in Sarawak
May 1963	cyclone in East Pakistan
July 1963	earthquake in Yugoslavia
September 1963	hurricane in West Indies (aid to Cuba, Tobago, and other islands)

In all these emergencies except that in Yugoslavia, WFP directed the sending of food supplies from the nearest country which had pledged the needed kinds of food to WFP. In one instance it borrowed stocks from a local importer and later replaced it with pledged food. In the case of the earthquake at Skopje, Yugoslavia, emergency relief poured in so quickly and in such quantity from governments and private relief agencies that WFP aid was not needed. However, WFP moved in afterwards to supply 1200 tons of food for 60,000 workers and their families engaged in removing debris and constructing provisional settlements for 100,000 inhabitants whose homes were destroyed.

A conclusion already reached in the WFP experiment is that its program should not be regarded as instantly ready to supply relief in emergencies. WFP is unable to move as fast as national governments or international relief agencies such as the International Red Cross to organize delivery and secure the shipping needed. And the commodities most in demand are those in shortest supply in WFP's larder of pledges, namely, protein foods, fats, and sugar. Also, the most immediate need in a disaster is for cash to buy needed supplies within the country or nearby, and this is also in short supply in WFP. However, WFP has found that it is well adapted to help in the second stage by replacing borrowed supplies and providing food help during reconstruction and rehabilitation.

Another conclusion already reached is that for the time being and probably for some time to come WFP is not going to be able to play a major role in helping countries build and maintain national food reserves as hedges against famine and violent price fluctuations. On the one hand, large countries require national food reserves far beyond the present or prospective resources of WFP, and, knowing that the surplus producing countries will come to their aid in case of real need, most of them so far prefer to let the richer countries pay storage costs and carry on the technical work of rotating and preserving stocks in good condition rather than undertake the responsibility themselves. On the other hand, small countries whose national food reserve requirements might conceivably be within the range of WFP resources do not as a rule have either the technical competence to store and maintain food reserves in good condition or the ability to administer effective price and reserve management policies. A couple of minor food reserve experiments are being undertaken by WFP in African countries but primarily as measures for price stabilization. If national food reserves are built up and maintained, therefore, it may have to continue to be done largely through bilateral deals with surplus countries, as was recommended by FAO in 1958.

At present the trend of thinking is that WFP cannot aim any time soon to become the agent of transfer of bulk supplies for general economic support such as are now carried on by the United States under Title I of Public Law 480. The surplus-producing countries are not likely to surrender control over huge bulk supplies to an international organ. However, things that do not appear possible frequently become possible with experience, accumulating knowledge, and the passage of time.

Surplus food as a direct aid in projects of economic and social development — this has emerged as the core of WFP, and its major emphasis during its experimental stage.

What of the future? This will be decided in 1965 after WFP completes three years of operations. It has problems. The low proportion of cash is one. The low proportion of proteins, rice, sugar, and some other items in its larder in relation to wheat, maize and dried milk is a second. And rising shipping costs are a third. These are certainly not insurmountable. However, to provide the basis for an informed decision on WFP's future, FAO and the United Nations have authorized five basic studies to be conducted by outside experts, and these are under way. WFP appears likely to become a permanent member of the U.N. family and to be endowed with considerably increased resources.

It is strictly as a member of the family that WFP operates. It is run by a joint U.N./FAO administrative unit. FAO provides it with headquarters office space; nearly half of WFP's administrative budget of $895,000 goes to reimburse FAO for technical, advisory and administrative services rendered; and FAO field staff helps both in framing projects and keeping an eye on their operations. But WFP works also in close cooperation with other members of the U.N. family. Its agents in the field are the U.N. Resident Representatives. It is under the joint supervision of FAO and the United Nations. Most of its programs other than emergency relief are either conducted in conjunction with other U.N. family projects, or they are follow-ups of those projects, or they are based on technical surveys and information produced in their operation.

There is very little that surplus food can do for international development that cash could not do. But some countries produce certain kinds of food more efficiently than others, and national surpluses, which tend to depress prices, are more willingly contributed for relief and development than cash. If they are used effectively in ways which do not disrupt normal commercial trade or discourage agricultural development, everybody is the gainer.

We have not yet reached the point where nations which can produce foods efficiently and at low cost deliberately plan surpluses for world use in meeting need, but the idea is beginning to be talked about. In fact, it is being urged by no less a person than Orville Freeman, U.S. Secretary of Agriculture. Where the idea will lead no one can tell. One thing is certain. We are only at the beginning of a long process in which the world production and use of food will be increasingly rationalized. WFP is in at the start.

CHAPTER 6

CAPITAL INVESTMENT IN AGRICULTURE, FORESTRY, AND FISHERIES

THE statesmen who planned the institutions of the postwar world were acutely aware of the need for a large, sustained flow of capital from the industrialized countries to those with less developed economies, and one of their first creations was the International Bank for Reconstruction and Development (the World Bank). Whether or not they ever had in mind that the Bank could or would play a major role in channelling capital into agricultural development, the fact is that the Bank has devoted most of its resources to communications, transportation, port modernization, power, and industry, with considerably less attention to agriculture. And for this, the Bank has been increasingly criticized.

During its first 18 years of operations up to June 1963, the World Bank devoted only $570 million or 8 per cent of its total loans of about $7 billion to agricultural projects, most of which were large-scale undertakings for irrigation, flood control and land clearance. However, there were numerous agricultural projects financed by the Bank which involved only small loans, and although only 8 per cent of the Bank's money was loaned for agricultural projects, 18 per cent of the total *number* of the Bank's loans have been for agriculture. Nevertheless, there is no denying that agriculture has been a second-class customer of the Bank.

Whatever the reasons for this, they are not to be found in lack of Bank authority. It is a misconception that the Bank can lend money only for "bankable" or self-liquidating projects, that is to say, for projects which promptly generate new revenues from which the loans can be repaid directly, such as the Bank-financed communications system in Ethiopia, a new central railroad in Colombia, and a high dam and power generator in Thailand. Most of the Bank's loans in the past have in fact been for projects of this kind, but not because of any legal requirement or even of formal Bank policy. Assurance of repayment from project revenues doubtless has influenced the Bank's preference, but there are other important reasons, and they are these: loans for construction projects are easier to design, operations are easier to supervise, and they are more *demonstrably* sound from an economic point of view than loans for agriculture or education. Agriculture is so diffused that results of investment are uncertain, and even though one knows that education eventually brings about increased economic activity, results cannot be proven and in any case are long deferred. To prove that it has not been wedded to self-liquidating projects the Bank points to its small loans for a considerable number of agricultural projects, and to several impressive loans to governments for general economic development. But figures prove the comparative neglect of agriculture.

Agriculture has been disadvantaged not only by the Bank's preferences as indicated above, but by the fact that the Bank's terms have been so sternly commercial as to discourage governments from borrowing for non-bankable enterprises. Interest rates have been $1\frac{1}{4}$ per cent higher than the cost of the Bank's borrowing on commercial markets, repayment of interest and capital has had to begin fairly promptly, and full repayment has usually been required within 20 years or less. Moreover, borrowing countries have had to find elsewhere the capital to cover nearly all the local costs of projects, for it was the Bank's stern aim to cover in its project loans only those costs requiring foreign exchange. These terms made it difficult for many countries to secure from the Bank the capital they needed. Dissatisfaction therefore grew, and pressures mounted for capital on easier terms. Throughout the 1950's, the less developed countries therefore raised their voices insistently in U.N. Councils for grants, or loans on much easier terms than those required by the World Bank, for "non-bankable" projects such as agriculture, water supply, sanitation, pilot housing, health, and education and training institutions. I have described briefly in an earlier chapter the controversy in the United Nations during the 1950's over the proposal for a Special U.N. Fund for Economic Development (SUNFED).

Although SUNFED never came into being, one result of the pressure and debate was the creation of the U.N. Special Fund for "pre-investment". Another was the creation of the International Development Association (IDA), which began operations in late 1960 with an authorized initial capital of $1 billion. Seventeen industrialized countries pledged to IDA three-quarters of the total sum in convertible currencies (the U.S. share was 32 per cent) and 51 less developed countries contributed the remainder, 10 per cent in gold or convertible currencies and 90 per cent in non-convertible national currencies. IDA is a close affiliate of the World Bank. Its president is also president of the Bank and its Board of Governors is almost identical with that of the Bank. In effect, it is the "soft loan window" of the World Bank. It may make exceptionally long-term loans, interest free for a certain number of years, repayable in foreign exchange. Also it may make loans repayable, wholly or partly, in inconvertible local currency, and i⁺ may make loans free of interest or at very low rates of interest. It is widely thought that IDA can make loans for *kinds* of projects different from those within the scope of the World Bank, but this is not true. That which distinguishes it most from the Bank is its easier terms.

IDA has been a good step in the right direction, but its resources of $1 billion for 5 years have been too small to meet the needs of a hundred countries. And like the World Bank, it has found difficulty in making loans for agricultural projects proportionate to agriculture's importance in the economies of the underdeveloped countries. In 3 years of operations, IDA made loans totalling nearly $500 million of which only 24 per cent by volume and 31 per cent by number of credits was for projects of direct benefit to agriculture. The Board of Governors in October 1963 authorized another $750 million for IDA to be spent over a period of *three* years. IDA will therefore be able to increase the pace of its lending. But more important for agriculture, the Bank and IDA have reached the conclusion that increased funds are not by themselves going to enable them to lend as much for agricultural projects as they would like or as much as is needed, and they have decided to take other steps to improve the situation.

The main obstacle to loans for agriculture, they have concluded, lies in the very nature of agriculture, and the difficulty of devising agricultural projects that are economically sound and can be effectively administered. Mr. George Woods, new President of the World Bank, has pointed out some of the difficulties: the large number of small, financially precarious farm units in any underdeveloped country, the low level of education in rural districts, weak incentives to higher productivity, and the inadequacy of government organization and personnel. Addressing the 1963 World Food Congress in Washington, he said, "It is possible for an outside agency (such as the World Bank) to install a power plant, build a road system or construct a harbor works and have them function for a while, even if local understanding of techniques of these installations is not widespread. But agriculture depends on the knowledge, the motivation, the effort of multitudes of human beings inside the developing countries." Technology for feeding the world exists, he asserted, but if the world is to know freedom from hunger the individual farmer must learn "freedom from habit" and adopt new methods. Beyond that, he said, agricultural development depends upon many physical variables, such as soil and plant characteristics, topography, climate, and the accidents of rainfall. Moreover, it depends upon transportation, crop storage, irrigation, credit institutions, and extension services.

These, of course, were problems FAO had known about and worked on for nearly 20 years. Accordingly, it is to FAO that the World Bank and IDA have turned for help.

Up until recently there has been a wide unbridged distance between the agricultural expertise of U.N.'s FAO and the operations and decision-making of the U.N. lending institutions — the World Bank and IDA. Cordial relations have been maintained between FAO and the Bank. The two have cooperated in joint surveys of development needs in industrial countries. FAO experts have participated in a large number of Bank missions and FAO experts have rendered a great deal of technical assistance to Bank projects. Moreover, FAO has always felt free to make suggestions and proposals to the Bank. Nevertheless, distance between the Bank and FAO has been maintained. Although FAO has been immersed in the needs of agricultural development and ceaselessly searching for means to meet them, the Bank has never relied upon FAO to propose projects and do the necessary technical and economic staff work in support of them, with the result that relations between them have not been fully fruitful.

Several important things have happened to bring about a change in this situation. One has been a fairly sudden recognition among government leaders and economists that progress in underdeveloped countries requires the modernization of agriculture. A second is that after nearly 20 years of operation the World Bank, as Mr. George Woods told his Board of Governors in September 1963, is beginning to exhaust "the more obvious and more easily manageable investment projects" (such as power plants, railroad and port expansion schemes, big irrigation projects) at a time when there is "a growing need for help in other sectors, in particular in agriculture, industry, and education, which often present much greater problems of appraisal, planning and management". In other words, the Bank is running out of kinds of obviously profitable construction projects which it has always favored. A third and most important thing that has happened is that FAO, as executor since 1959 of a large and growing number of pre-investment projects financed by the Special Fund, has added enormously to its knowledge of investment possibilities in agriculture, fisheries and forestry. FAO/Special Fund projects are aimed at preparing the way for capital investment, and a great many of them have already disclosed investment opportunities.

Mr. Woods told his Boards of Governors quite frankly at their annual meeting in September 1963 that the Bank and IDA were going to have to give more support to agriculture (including agricultural education) on a much broader front and on more liberal terms than in the past, and that in so doing they should take full advantage of the knowledge and experience of other international organizations. Hearing this, Dr. Sen, Director General of FAO, lost no time in getting in touch with Mr. Woods! Very shortly Mr. Woods visited Rome to discuss a closer relationship with FAO, and subsequently sent three senior officials to negotiate formal arrangements. The result was an agreement between FAO and the World Bank/IDA, signed by Mr. Woods on 30 March 1964, and Dr. Sen on 2 April, under which the agricultural knowledge and experience of FAO are to be used more effectively to bring about a greater flow of investment capital into projects designed to increase agricultural production.

The essence of the agreement, as Mr. Woods expressed it in a letter to Dr. Sen, is that the Bank expects "to rely on FAO not only as a major source of technical and management assistance for member countries but also to perform much of the agricultural work involved in the identification, preparation, appraisal and end-use supervision of projects and programs financed by us". As Dr. Sen expressed it in a letter to the FAO Council, "The Bank will rely on FAO for the extension of its agricultural activities, and FAO will look to the Bank for the eventual financing of projects."

These are more than expressions of hope and intent. The agreement between the Bank and FAO provides for assembling promptly within the FAO Secretariat a team of high caliber specialists in agricultural investment which, with the support of the FAO professional staff, will concentrate upon helping countries identify and prepare projects for Bank financing. On its own, the Bank is intensifying its search for promising agricultural projects by means of survey missions, and hereafter these missions are to consult FAO on possible projects and agricultural investment priorities, and the missions will frequently include an FAO staff member or consultant as adviser. FAO will help appraise agricultural projects considered by the Bank and help supervise the execution and operation of those whose financing the Bank undertakes. FAO is to provide the technical assistance needed for Bank projects, with the Bank paying the cost plus 12 per cent to cover FAO's administrative or overhead expenses. The Bank will pay FAO travel and subsistence expenses in connection with Bank missions. Moreover, of the direct staff and other headquarters costs to FAO of the cooperative program, the Bank agrees to pay a large part. In the 2 years 1964–5 FAO will pay $200,000 and the Bank up to $600,000 for total costs which, it is estimated, may reach $800,000.

A cooperative FAO/World Bank investment program can have far-reaching consequences for world agriculture. As far as FAO is concerned, it relieves frustrations which have been accumulating for years, and opens the doors to a new release of creative energy. Confronted in daily operations by the failure of world food supply to keep pace with rapidly increasing population, FAO has been increasingly unhappy about the distance that has existed between its accumulation of knowledge, on the one hand, and the U.N. capital-lending process on the other. It could only make surveys, and launch investment proposals on uncertain seas. For its part the Bank, realizing the desperate need for more investment in agriculture, has grown increasingly dissatisfied with its inability to work out more sound projects for agricultural loans. It was spending more and more time preparing agricultural proposals and still had insufficient agricultural staff to make enough headway. And all the time, the needed technical experts were in FAO.

Both FAO and the Bank are therefore enthusiastic about the new arrangements. The joint "team" in FAO, backed by the experience and expertise of the entire Organization, will in effect work out an investment program for consideration by the Bank. Each institution will become intimately aware of the policies and procedures of the other. It will make an enormous psychological and practical difference to FAO field staff "to know that they have a banker at their elbow", as one Bank official expressed it. It will also make a big difference to the Bank to know that projects presented to it have been worked out and approved by the joint FAO/Bank team. Looking back over agricultural surveys done in the past, FAO officials now realize how much sharper and more specific their recommendations and proposals would have been if they had then had a direct channel to the Bank.

The President of the World Bank has said publicly that the Bank is not only going to channel a greater proportion of its funds into agriculture, but that it is going to "liberalize" its loan terms for agriculture projects. This means two things. It means that the Bank will finance not only the foreign exchange costs of the projects it approves, but also a more liberal proportion of the local costs as well. It also means that the Bank will allow longer periods of grace between the time the loan is made and the time when interest and principal repayment must begin.

Decision-making regarding loans will remain the exclusive province of the Bank. The new Bank policies, and the new arrangements with FAO for combined staff work, should lead to a considerably increased flow of capital for agricultural, forestry, and fishery development.

PART III

The Food and Agriculture Organization
of the United Nations

CHAPTER I

THE FAO "REGULAR PROGRAM"

THE central international repository of knowledge relating to agriculture, forestry, and fisheries, and the chief agency of the United Nations for disseminating it, is the Food and Agriculture Organization of the United Nations (FAO). Conceived in 1943 at a conference in Hot Springs, Virginia, called by President Franklin D. Roosevelt, and chartered at a conference in Quebec, Canada, in October 1945, FAO operated for several years on an annual budget of $5 million, a budget which largely confined its technical staff to FAO headquarters which were first established in Washington, D.C., and moved to Rome, Italy, in 1951.* Its activities were at first restricted to making technical studies, collecting statistics and disseminating them via publications and correspondence, calling and attending conferences, establishing technical commissions, and dispatch of occasional field study missions.†

Then in 1950 came the beginning of change. Powerful world currents and events disclosed critical urgent needs for development help in three underdeveloped continents, and led by the United States, which itself embarked upon a large program of bilateral aid, the United Nations and its family of organizations stepped up its response to the need. In the years since, "response to need" has evolved into a worldwide program of development to help narrow the large and growing gap between incomes in poor nations and those

* For accounts of the conception, chartering, and early functioning of FAO, see *The Story of FAO*, by Gove Hambidge, Van Nostrand, New York, London, and Toronto, 1955. See also *So Bold An Aim*, written by Lamartine Yates and published by FAO in 1955.

† FAO was nevertheless able for a while to carry on certain limited field activities in help to a few governments in 1947, and after, with $1,140,000 which it unexpectedly inherited from the U.N. Relief and Rehabilitation Administration when it went out of business.

in the rich. In these circumstances, and given the overwhelming actual and potential importance of agriculture, forestry, and fisheries in the less developed countries, FAO has grown from a small technical agency to a major U.N. development agency disposing of funds in excess of $50 million a year and leading a worldwide campaign against hunger.

In earlier chapters we have seen how FAO works with other members of the U.N. family to accomplish common purposes. But the foundation of all FAO help to the world's agriculture, forestry, and fisheries is its "Regular Program", and to that we now turn attention.

The word "program" is one of the most overworked and misused words in any language. According to the dictionary and general understanding, a program is a definite plan of future procedure. The FAO Regular Program includes a plan of future procedure, but it is much more than that. It is in effect the central work of FAO covered by the independent FAO budget. It is so called to distinguish it from the worldwide field activities carried on with U.N. funds supplied from outside the FAO budget. These additional U.N. funds are supplied for specific services requested by governments, and their control remains outside FAO. However, they provide FAO with most of its field staff, and in effect, field operations have become an extension of the Regular Program. The activities of headquarters and field staff are so enmeshed that it is often hard to tell them apart.

The core of FAO is its technical and economic staff, most of which is stationed at headquarters in Rome. Their knowledge, their studies, their worldwide professional contacts are of the essence of the Organization. This is necessarily so, for as we have seen, FAO exists primarily to bring about an increase, an interchange, a transfer of knowledge. In Chapter 2 of Part I of this book I have tried to give some idea of the depth and technical complexity of agriculture, forestry, and fisheries. In these fields FAO specialists must not only command accumulated knowledge, but they must keep abreast of rapid technical and scientific advances. They must know intimately conditions in member countries. They must also know who, throughout the world, are the most competent and up-to-date professionals in each speciality, for they have the responsibility for recruiting the experts sent by the United Nations to aid governments in the solution of their problems. Moreover, they must advise, support and backstop these experts while they are in the field.

The technical and economic staff of FAO is grouped in the Technical Department and the Department of Economic and Social Affairs. These two departments contain ten divisions and no less than forty-one branches covering technical fields. And of course each branch handles many specialities. Together, the two departments account for about two-thirds of the professionals employed by FAO under the Regular Program.

This staff of professional specialists must serve the 106 countries which are members and the six which are associate members of FAO. Its activities must be meshed with the desires, the national plans, and the operating realities of governments. Its work must be conducted within the limits of the program, budget and priorities established by the Director General and the FAO Conference. It must observe the policies and priorities decided upon in the U.N. General Assembly and the U.N. Economic and Social Council. It must conform to the procedures and regulations of EPTA, the Special Fund, UNICEF, WFP and those other members of the U.N. family who provide most of the funds for FAO field services. FAO work also requires extensive travel, and arrangements for and attendance at hundreds of international meetings, which are generally conducted in the three official languages, English, French and Spanish, with simultaneous translation. It demands conference papers and other publications by the ton, also in three languages. Finally, it requires, as already mentioned, recruitment and back-stopping of well over a thousand field experts and half again as many Fellows working on projects meshed in with its Regular Program.

Clearly, then, the central work of the specialists in the spread of knowledge requires careful direction and management, elaborate policy and budget planning and control, and close, continuous contact and coordination with member governments, with FAO regional office and country representatives, and with other U.N.

agencies. It also demands extensive administrative, legal and information services. The bulk of these functions and services must be covered by the FAO Regular Program budget.

That FAO promotes the spread of knowledge under the Regular Program through international conferences* and technical meetings is a statement that rolls easily and often off tongue and pen, but it conveys little reality. Perhaps, to begin with, it is somewhat more meaningful to say that FAO publishes each year a Directory of Standing Committees and Technical and Regional Bodies, and that the issue of 1 April 1964 contained more than a hundred such bodies then operative. They are called variously Councils, Commissions, Committees, Subcommittees, Advisory Groups, Working Parties, Panels of Experts — all established by the FAO governing conference. To take a few at random, there is an international Working Party on Mediterranean Pasture and Fodder Development, a Committee on Pesticides, an Indo-Pacific Fisheries Council, an International Rice Commission, a Soil Resources Committee for South America, an African Commission on Agricultural Statistics, an Advisory Committee on Marine Resources Research, a Working Party on Animal Production and Health in the Near East, a Cocoa Study Group, a Working Party on Consolidation of Land Holdings, and more than ninety others. Most of the agricultural, fishery, and forestry problems of greatest concern to government in each continent or region are covered by these bodies, and the door is always open for governments to ask for the establishment of others.

Each of these standing bodies assembles, some regularly and often, some sporadically, in meetings held all over the world. Each requires servicing by FAO, some continuously, some intermittently. For each meeting of each body technical papers and studies must be prepared, and from most of them papers, recommendations, and studies emerge. The meetings are attended by experts from many countries, some being government officials, some not. Invariably,

* We shall leave for consideration in the next chapter the controlling, policy-making, budget-voting FAO Conference which meets once each two years, and the advisory regional FAO conferences, which also meet biennially.

they are organized by FAO and attended by the FAO officials and specialists concerned.

FAO spreads knowledge not only through meetings of these continuing bodies, but also through international training centers, seminars, and fellowships. At seminars small groups of senior officials in policy-making positions and high level technicians from different countries, usually but not always within a region, meet together for a week or so to exchange views and experiences on common problems. More junior officials and technicians attend training centers lasting 3 to 6 weeks or longer, where they not only exchange views and experiences but attend organized lectures and demonstrations. From 1950 to 1963, FAO sponsored or co-sponsored 249 seminars and training centers in various parts of the world attended by 7858 persons. FAO organizes most of these affairs, provides lecturers and staff, and prepares the needed technical papers. The country which serves as host provides the necessary physical facilities and secretarial services. Transportation and living expenses for the participants are paid for sometimes from FAO Regular Program funds, or more often with funds supplied by EPTA, the Special Fund, or one or more of the other members of the U.N. family which may act as co-sponsors.

Here are a few examples.

Sweden was host in 1959 for a training course on mechanized forest operations which was attended by thirty-two participants from Austria, Bulgaria, Greece, Poland, Portugal and the U.S.S.R. A seminar on agricultural cooperatives in Denmark was attended by high level officials from countries as widely scattered as Basutoland, Burma, Haiti, Tunisia, and Vietnam. In Asia, centers for farm management have been held each year since 1956 in host countries which have included Japan, Vietnam, Thailand, and the Philippines. Colombia has been host to trainees from Latin American countries for instruction in modern techniques of inland fisheries. Eighteen Near East seminars and training centers have been held in Cairo alone on subjects including the collection of agricultural statistics, barley breeding, agricultural extension, marketing, nutrition, and agricultural development planning.

FAO's basic budget provides for only a few fellowships each year and they are awarded for advanced research and training to men who are already recognized in their field. These are called André Mayer Fellowships after the distinguished French scientist who played an important part in the creation of FAO and served as first Chairman of its Council. Nevertheless, FAO operates a large training fellowship program with funds provided mostly by EPTA, but also by other members of the U.N. family and by private foundations and individual governments. From 1951 through 1963 FAO awarded 3341 such fellowships, and most of these were directly related to the work of FAO experts in field projects. For example, a country needing to promote the local canning of fruits and vegetables has asked an FAO expert to come and survey the situation. He has done so, and has made certain recommendations. But there are not enough trained technicians in the country to carry them out. The country therefore asks for fellowships for promising young men who go abroad, study, investigate, and return to put the recommended program into effect — and to train others. Special Fund pre-investment projects executed by FAO usually involve the training of people, and increasingly they provide fellowships for younger men who then return from their foreign studies and play an active role in carrying on the work initiated by outside experts.

It would be difficult to overestimate the importance of FAO conferences, technical meetings, seminars, training centers, and training fellowships to the countries of Asia, Africa and Latin America. Consider first those seminars which bring together around a table senior officials and administrators (but, usually, not the political chiefs) of the ministries of agriculture and development agencies. To begin to appreciate the significance of these seminars it is necessary to try to imagine the sense of isolation which assails high officials in the underdeveloped countries as they face the complex, mountainous problems of applying modern science and technology to production from land, sea, and forest. With public expectations and pressures mounting, with too little experience in the government, too few institutions, too few trained people, they need help. At FAO meetings they acquire knowledge, and receive advice and help in solving their problems. Equally important, they derive comfort and confidence simply from talking over problems which they share with colleagues in other countries.

But even when senior officials know what to do and have some idea of how it should be done, their hourly, daily problem is the shortage of men with enough training to do what needs to be done. FAO training centers and fellowships are a beginning of the answer. They are far too few, they reach too few people, and they last too short a time. They are no substitute for a full education in a first-class agricultural college or technical institute. But they are a tremendous help. There is no ministry of agriculture, or any forestry or fishery department in the whole of Asia, Africa, and Latin America which has not been benefited by FAO training programs, and few in which FAO trainees and Fellows do not now hold important positions.

It would be foolish to suppose that all the 12,000 FAO trainees and Fellows have benefited from the opportunities afforded them. But most of them have. Returning to their countries with increased knowledge, confidence and prestige, with contacts established with fellow workers in other countries, they play significant roles in the development of their countries and the further spread of knowledge.

While one can be sure that a week's seminar and a 3 to 6 week's training course increases to some degree the effectiveness of those who attend them, direct results are nevertheless difficult to trace. But FAO files bulge with records and accomplishments of fellowship holders.

An Iranian who studied cereal breeding for 15 months in Canada on a fellowship is now supervising Iran's wheat and barley improvement program and teaching plant genetics at the Faculty of Agriculture in Tehran.

A Fellow from India who investigated horticulture in England, France, and Italy returned to his country to introduce a variety of new plant stocks and a new system of olive cultivation.

An Egyptian, holder of an FAO fellowship for studies of agricultural machinery and testing in the United Kingdom, the Netherlands, Sweden, and Germany, is now head of the Agricultural Engineering Department of the University of Alexandria.

E

The training which a Fellow from Japan received in Europe has contributed greatly to his government's reclamation of peat land.

A Burmese who studied animal nutrition in Australia and New Zealand under a fellowship is now lecturer in the Animal Husbandry Department of Burma's Veterinary College.

A bright young man who is now doing splendid work as Director of Senegal's Institute of Food Technology got his training in France and Italy on a FAO fellowship and in the United States with the assistance of the U.S. Agency for International Development.

Forestry, fishery and livestock development in Chile is being carried on to a considerable extent by men who studied abroad on FAO fellowships or attended FAO training centers, and by men which they, in turn, trained.

Such examples run into thousands.

Studies, research, surveys, the collection and analysis of statistics, the gathering and collation of technical information from all over the world — these are foundations of FAO's work. And to be of use, the results of these activities must of course be published and distributed, usually in three languages. It is not surprising, therefore, that in 1964 FAO printed some 80 to 90 million pages and that its printing and publication costs, entirely aside from the costs of preparing the material, constitute about a tenth of the Regular Program budget.

Most FAO publications are directed chiefly to government administrators, technicians, and other specialists throughout the world concerned with agriculture, fisheries, forestry and nutrition. There are FAO periodicals such as the Monthly Bulletin of Agricultural Economics and Statistics, Cocoa Statistics, Unasylva, World Fisheries Abstracts, Food and Agricultural Legislation, the FAO Plant Protection Bulletin, the Statistical Yearbooks of agricultural, fisheries and forestry products. These constitute a world intelligence service on production, prices and trade relating to nearly every commodity that is used to feed, clothe and house the human race. FAO's major annual publication, *The State of Food and Agriculture*, is a basic world document in which conditions are recorded and trends analyzed. This publication is of great importance to governments and is used throughout the world as a valuable source of information.

Then there is a steady stream of technical studies, glossaries and abstracts which, if they are of wide enough interest, are published and put on sale all over the world. To date, about 700 of these have been published, with titles such as: "Improving Agricultural Tenancy"; "Land Tenure"; "Trichomonas Foetus Infection in Cattle"; Soil Surveys for Land Development"; "National Food Reserve Policies in Underdeveloped Countries"; "Modern Fishing Gear of the World"; "Handling Forest Tree Seed"; "Social Welfare in Rural Communities"; and more than 690 others!

Most FAO experts who go to help countries with particular problems write reports of their findings and recommendations. Sometimes these are published for the benefit of other countries with similar problems, depending upon whether the government of the chief country concerned gives its approval. Published reports of this nature now number about 1700.

A special series of Basic Studies was begun in 1961 under the aegis of the Freedom from Hunger Campaign, intended for a wider readership, including such titles as "Population and Food Supply"; "Nutrition and Working Efficiency"; "Animal Disease and Human Health"; "Development Through Food"; and "Aspects of Economic Development". Some of these are being issued by other members of the U.N. family as their contribution to the Campaign.

Beyond these categories, FAO prints and distributes so many thousands of conference documents, working papers, and special reports that any guess at the number would be wild and misleading. Nevertheless, it is impossible to please all the representatives of all the government all the time. On the floor of the FAO Conference one hears grumbles such as "Why has this report been released in French and not in Spanish", or "Unfortunately this working paper was not received by my government in time to study it properly." But you also hear complaints from members at conferences that they are being swamped with papers.

As one ranking Ministry of Agriculture official in an African country talked to me in his office I could see that his table was covered with FAO publications and his bookshelves filled with them. "One of the things we like most about these publications", he said, "is that they give us information and experience from various parts of the world. This enables us to get ideas and apply them to our own conditions. Take for example", he continued, "the study 'Animal Breeding Under Tropical and Sub-Tropical Conditions'. This publication is a help to us and many other countries in Africa, Asia and Latin America in our efforts to improve our livestock. Also, the *FAO Yearbook of Production and Trade Statistics* contains information which has been of help to us in making our development plans. These are rather obvious", he continued, "but there is another important benefit from these statistical publications which is not generally recognized. FAO requires that we and other member countries present our statistics and other agricultural information according to a prescribed pattern. This builds up a common way of reporting and a common way of thinking about agricultural matters. It affects profoundly the outlook of ministries and departments of agriculture in all countries."

These, then, are the central intelligence and training activities of FAO, most of which, except for the fellowships, are financed under Regular Program budget and conducted by FAO's specialized staff.

The first day I spent inside the portals of FAO in Rome I was struck by the number of times the term "Regular Program" was mentioned in conversation, usually with touchy overtones. In succeeding weeks I became aware that a special sensitivity and protectiveness about the Regular Program pervades the whole institution at all levels. I tried, then, to get some conception of the Regular Program as distinct from other FAO activities. It was difficult to do.

It took a long time to discover that the term "Regular Program" is frequently used very loosely and means different things to different people, and different things to the same people at different times. It is sometimes used to refer to the technical and administrative staff at headquarters and regional offices, as apart from the staff engaged in field operations. It is sometimes used to denote the "original" FAO activities described in this chapter, as distinguished from the field services rendered to governments in cooperation with other U.N. programs. It is sometimes used to mean FAO budget itself, apart from the funds supplied for FAO operations by other members of the U.N. family of organizations. And it is sometimes used to mean FAO staff, activities and services at headquarters and in the field, paid for out of the FAO budget as voted by the FAO Conference. The latter is the only meaning of the Regular Program which, technically, is *wholly* correct.

But why the sensitivity and protectiveness toward the Regular Program and the touchiness with regard to the programs financed by other sources? Bafflement grew as I discovered that the Regular Program staff spends nearly half its time in work connected with field operations, and that the Regular Program activities described in this chapter — studies, conferences, technical meetings, seminars, training centers — are, quite properly, intertwined with field operations. Why then, consider the Regular Program as something apart? In time, a number of answers became reasonably clear.

To begin with the trivial, there are scattered throughout FAO a few old timers who have a nostalgia for FAO as it was before the other U.N. agencies began to "thrust new opportunities and responsibilities upon it". They are inclined to resent the new, glamorous field operations which seem to overshadow the original activities of the FAO Regular Program. Others in FAO tend to regard the older activities of the Regular Program as "ours" and the field programs as "theirs", because "ours" are wholly controlled and financed by FAO while "theirs" are financed, and at least partially controlled, by other agencies. And yet, there has always been competition between the technical divisions to get EPTA funds to expand activity in their different fields of work! The old-fashioned attitudes are not very important, and certainly are not shared by most of the officers of the Organization, who have welcomed all opportunities to extend services to the world regardless of the sources of the money and the difficulties of sharing policy control with other members of the U.N. family. Demands by underdeveloped countries for services continue to mount, the food situation in the world continues to deteriorate because of disastrous population growth, and the need for increased aid to agricultural production spurs FAO each day. All opportunities to increase field operations are therefore grasped with both hands.

The real reasons for sensitivity about the Regular Program are as follows: Without superior competence in technical fields, FAO has no special *raison d'être*. The technical and economic staff of FAO is being loaded increasingly with operating responsibilities in connection with field programs financed by other members of the U.N. family, and thus loaded, it is in danger of losing its superior technical competence. Specialists overburdened with operating responsibilities are not able to keep up with professional literature and contacts, or keep abreast of the latest developments in their fields. Moreover, they are not able to make all the studies needed and cannot give governments all the advice they are entitled to have under the Regular Program.

Then why not increase the staff sufficiently to ease the problem? There's the rub! Increasing the regular budget is a painful process, as we shall see in the next chapter, and lags far behind operating need. Moreover, it lags behind the pace of field operations as determined by other U.N. agencies, notably the U.N. Special Fund.

The original FAO budget fixed by the first FAO Conference for 1946 was $5 million per year. Eight years later, in 1954, FAO's Regular Program expenditures were only $5.5 million. In the interval, world prices had nearly doubled, FAO's membership had increased from 45 to 71 countries, demands for services had greatly increased, and FAO had assumed responsibilities for worldwide technical assistance with funds supplied by EPTA. Nevertheless EPTA funds did not cover the full costs of backstopping services, and the work of the field experts inevitably resulted in greater demands upon FAO. By 1956 FAO/EPTA technical assistance had increased to $8 million, and FAO regular budget expenditures to only $6.4 million.

What happened thereafter is shown in Table 1, below.

The Special Fund started operations in 1959. Its payments to FAO for executing field projects began in 1960, and thereafter burgeoned. In 1964, FAO/Special Fund project expenditures will amount to nearly as much as the entire FAO Regular Program. The Special Fund pays as overhead costs to FAO 11 per cent on all personnel recruited and 3 per cent on equipment supplied, but the payments are included in the Special Fund lump sum figures, and they do not fully cover backstopping services. In November 1961 the FAO Conference approved the first really substantial increase in the FAO Regular Program budget, and in November 1963 it approved another substantial increase — to $38.8 million for the 2 years 1964 and 1965, that is to say to $19.4 million annually.

TABLE 1. EXPENDITURE OF FUNDS — FAO
(Millions of U.S. dollars)

Source of funds	1954	1956	1958	1960	1962	1964*
Regular Program	5.5	6.4	7.9	9.3	12.5	19.4
EPTA	4.7	8.0	8.4	8.4	11.5	10.4
U.N. Special Fund	—	—	—	0.7	8.1	19.0†
Trust Funds, etc.	0.2	0.5	0.9	1.0	2.3	4.0
	10.4	14.9	17.2	19.4	35.4	52.8

* All figures for 1964 are not expenditures but budget estimates.

† Although $19 million is allocated to FAO for Special Fund Projects in 1964, it is not likely that more than $17 million will be spent.

Note: Part of the increase in the Regular Program expenditures in 1960 as compared with 1958 is due to the fact that EPTA overhead payments to FAO, about $1 million a year which had previously been handled separately, were included for the first time in the Regular Program budget.

A more detailed picture of FAO's current operations is seen in Table 2, below. Clearly, FAO has come a long way in the last 10 years. From a small technical agency with an annual budget of $5 million a year, it has grown into a worldwide U.N. development agency whose 1964 expenditures in service to 112 countries for agriculture, forestry and fisheries will reach well over $50 million. This total includes, and is dependent upon, the $19.4 million of the FAO Regular Program budget.

TABLE 2. ESTIMATED PROGRAM 1964
(Millions of U.S. dollars)

Source of funds	Headquarters and Regional Offices	Field Operations	Total
Regular Program	18.8	0.6	19.4
EPTA	(1.1)*	10.4†	10.4*
U.N. Special Fund	2.0	17.0	19.0‖
UNICEF	—	1.3	1.3
WFP	0.4‡	—§	0.4
FFHC and Trust Funds	0.8	1.5	2.3
	22.0	30.8	52.8

* Lump sum allocation for headquarters' costs ($1,107,000) included in the Regular Program total.

† 1964 project allocations. Working capital and Reserve Fund authorizations ($740,000 to date) are excluded.

‡ Represents reimbursement of agency costs to FAO.

§ WFP projects ($36,020,000) are administered by the Executive Director, WFP.

‖ See note to Table 1.

To complete the picture of FAO, the total FAO staff, as of 31 December 1963, is shown in Table 3. These figures cover all home and field staff, including technical experts and project personnel paid for by EPTA, the Special Fund, and other sources.

TABLE 3. FAO STAFF: FILLED POSTS INCLUDING WORLD FOOD PROGRAM
(31 December 1963)

Location	Professional	General Service	Total
Headquarters	664	1305	1969
Regional Offices	112	253	365
Field Projects	1071	85	1156
	1847	1643	3490

FAO had $21.5 million in 1964 to support its headquarters and regional staff, numbering more than 2334 people, to carry on worldwide technical and economic intelligence activities, to plan and negotiate field projects, recruit for them, service them, and backstop them, and to coordinate the whole into integrated development programs in scores of countries. Of this sum, $3.8 million consisted of "overhead" payments by other members of the U.N. family in connection with field projects. But according to a survey made by Director General Sen, nearly one half of the total time of all Rome headquarters and regional office staff is taken up with projects whose field costs are financed by other U.N. agencies. Thus there is a squeeze on the Regular Program budget and staff.

Meanwhile, the underdeveloped countries, trying to make headway against rapidly growing populations with rising expectations, have steadily increased their calls for Regular Program help. The FAO Conference of November 1961 approved a considerably increased budget for 1962 and 1963. Nevertheless, of the 486 recommendations for action made by FAO technical conferences during those 2 years, 122 worthy of support could not be considered because of lack of funds, although it is hoped to include some of these in future EPTA requests. The projects which could not be adopted for lack of funds included: regional training courses on plant protection in the Middle East; a supervised credit pilot project in Latin America; a seminar on animal husbandry education in Latin America; and a basic program of research for curing rice in the field.

Meanwhile, other requests were pouring in.

CHAPTER 2

THE DIRECTOR GENERAL, THE TONE, AND THE STAFF

As the home seat of FAO, Rome has an advantage which was probably not considered by those who chose it. Surrounded by the visible ruins of Empire, reminded daily that civilizations are transitory, those who live and work in Rome cannot avoid acquiring a certain amount of useful historical perspective. At a time in world history when population growth is pressing hard against food supply; at a time when the 2 billion people who are poor and hungry are realizing they need no longer be poor and hungry and expect not to remain so; at a time when the long under-privileged peoples of the earth in Asia, Africa and Latin America, most of these with new-found independence, are jostling for their place in the sun; at a time when civilizations are in flux and the whole world under the threat of nuclear annihilation — at times such as ours, those who direct the world organization charged with helping nations increase food supply and raise living standards have need of historical perspective.

White, undistinguished save for bulk, and self-conscious, the FAO headquarters building in Rome squats stolidly between the majestic ruins of the Baths of Caracalla and the vast, deserted site of the ancient Circus Maximus. Immediately across the way at an angle are the extensive remains, touchingly beautiful in decay, of the fabulous palaces on the Palatine Hill which once housed the rulers of Imperial Rome. Even nearer is a church from whose site St. Augustine departed in A.D. 596 with forty monks to Christianize pagan England. Within 5 minutes' walk are the broken columns of the Roman Forum, and the familiar sight of the Colosseum, built on the site of Nero's lake. On every hand, throughout the city, are the reminders of ancient power and grandeur long since vanished.

On the plains immediately outside Rome, segments of once proud aqueducts suddenly appear, start marching, and abruptly vanish. Imperial Rome's once bustling seaport of nearby Ostia, upon which once converged a steady stream of ships bearing grain and other produce from all over the Empire, is now rubble scarcely noticed as one drives to the airport or the beach. And from whence did these food-bearing ships come? From the lands of North Africa, the Near East, Asia Minor — the granaries of ancient Rome. And what are those lands now? They are deserts or denuded and eroded hills, their forests gone, their elaborate irrigation works buried, their fabulous cities vanished. Two thousand years before the Romans built their Empire, at least as far back as Abraham, a great Sumerian civilization flourished in the lush, fertile lands of Mesopotamia watered by means of elaborate irrigation works from the Tigris and Euphrates rivers. All this had disappeared long before the Romans came on the scene.

Rome provides generous food for thought about the future of our today's civilization, but it gives no solace to those inclined to take comfort from the thought that history moves slowly. The main building which houses FAO in Rome was constructed by Mussolini after the conquest of Ethiopia to house his Ministry of Colonies. A few years later he was dead and his empire dissolved. The piazza in front of the FAO Conference building is adorned by the venerable Obelisk of Axum brought by the Italian dictator from the ancient capital of Ethiopia in 1937. But Italy's former Ministry of Colonies is now international territory donated to FAO by the Italian Government, and the flags of 112 nations fly on the side of FAO facing the Viale Aventino. They include, of course, the flag of Ethiopia. And speaking of colonies, there just are not many of them anywhere any more. They have disappeared in less than 20 years.

There is nothing plush about FAO headquarters. The Conference halls, housed in a separate building constructed for FAO, are plain, adequate — nothing more. And there are not enough of them. Many of the Committees must meet at Conference time in rooms far from adequate. As for the main office building — the former Ministry of Colonies — its interior suggests some overgrown administration and faculty office building in a large midwestern university in the United States. The sole concession to grandeur and style in the entire building is the long, spacious promenade deck on the top floor with an incomparable view of old Rome, and of the countryside extending southeast as far as the Alban Hills. One needs the view and the promenade after having lunch in the enormous, noisy cafeteria just off the deck, a cafeteria, incidentally, which would not flatter a large modern factory. There is, however, a restaurant with table service on the same floor, which is quieter, pleasant, and open to all who wish to pay the higher prices.

The staff of FAO, recruited from some sixty different member countries, is about as international as it can be. Members are of all colors and speak many tongues, but there is a surprising uniformity of language, the language of international development, the language of FAO. The exotic is so rare in FAO precincts that the tall, handsome, turbaned Sikh, the beautiful Indian lady in her sari, the portly delegate from Kenya with his magnificent mutton chops straight out of the Victorian era, and the gaily gowned Nigerian, excite nearly as much admiration and interest among the FAO staff when they turn up at Conference time as they would on the street in Peoria, Illinois.

It is difficult to characterize an international professional staff which consists of engineers, veterinarians, agronomists, economists, social workers, biologists, professors, scientists and technologists of many varieties, and administrators. One strongly suspects that the engineers have often had mud on their shoes, that the agronomists have had hay in their hair, and that the veterinarians have stayed up many nights with sick cows. Nevertheless, the professional staff as a whole gives the impression that it might well constitute the faculty of some large international agricultural university. This is not surprising, for many of them have higher academic degrees or at one time or another have been professors.

The man who chooses the FAO staff and directs its worldwide activities, the man who sets the FAO tone, the man who in name and in fact produces the FAO show, subject to the directives issued and the limitations imposed by the FAO Conference, is the Director

General, Dr. Binay Ranjan Sen. Chosen by the FAO Conference in a Special Session held in Rome in September 1956 Dr. Sen was re-elected in 1959 and again for a 4-year term in November 1963. He is now serving his eighth year. Dr. Sen was the first Asian to be chosen to direct one of the main organs of the U.N. family, and after 7 years, he is generally regarded in U.N. circles as one of the best of the U.N. directors. Without question, he is the most effective Director General FAO ever had.

Looking at the barest and briefest facts of B. R. Sen's life and career, it is curious to note how they conspired to equip him for a job which requires some knowledge of agriculture, familiarity with the ways of national government administration, experience in international diplomacy and U.N. affairs, and above all, knowledge of the realities, the feelings, the aspirations of both the peoples of the underprivileged countries of the world and those of the more privileged. Born in India in 1898, son of a well-to-do Indian doctor, B. R. Sen had the advantage of an education both at Calcutta University and at Oxford. Joining the Indian Civil Service in 1922 in his country ruled by Great Britain, he served for many years as a District Officer in Bengal, coming into close contact there with the needs, capacities and the hopes of people who live on the farms and in rural villages. After that he rose in the government service, holding many important posts in the Bengal and Central Governments, including the Secretaryship of the Indian Food Ministry. In 1942, when a massive typhoon brought death and calamity to many tens of thousands in Bengal, Sen, then Revenue Secretary in the Government of Bengal, assumed direction of the relief work. Starvation and epidemics which could have been immeasurably worse than the original disaster were held in check. The next year a famine in Bengal took toll of 3 million lives, and Sen, who had risen to the post of Director General of Food for all India, set up a nationwide rationing system, which contrary to general expectation, worked.

After India's independence, Dr. Sen went to Washington as Minister in the Indian Embassy and in subsequent years served as the Ambassador of India to Italy, Yugoslavia, the United States and

Japan. During these years in the Indian Diplomatic Service, he found time to represent India at many international conferences, leading Indian delegations to the General Assembly of the United Nations, the Security Council, and the Economic and Social Council. In 1948 he had been a member of the Indian delegation to the FAO Conference. Returning as head of the Indian delegation to the FAO Conference in 1956, he was chosen to be Director General of FAO. He was remarkably well prepared for the job.

When Sen assumed the mantle he was in position to know that it was an extremely difficult one to wear. To say that FAO was not in a very happy condition at the time is a vast understatement. The Organization had not known for so long where it was going that morale was at rock bottom. FAO had operated on a Regular Program budget of $5 million a year for a period of 10 years during which prices and costs of nearly everything had just about doubled, and in 1956 the budget had been increased to only $6.6 million. Although the technical assistance program was increasing each year with funds supplied by EPTA, their activities were for the most part unrelated and unplanned. The Organization was sadly in need of aggressive direction.

The first Director General of FAO, Lord John Boyd Orr, was a Scotsman of great presence, determination and prodigious and well-merited reputation. He was one of the founders of FAO, his voice carried weight in international circles, and he personified the dynamic. But Lord Boyd Orr's ideas were far in advance of his time and his efforts were doomed to frustration. With energy and single-ness of purpose he aspired to bring about the creation of a world food board which would acquire food reserves and direct the movement of food supplies as needed. Faced with discouraging reactions at the first FAO Conference in 1946, he came up subse-quently with modifications of his original idea, but met with no greater success, and after being attacked at the FAO Conference by the chief delegate of the United Kingdom, he resigned early in 1948, a disappointed man. The major food-producing countries of the world were not then, and are not now, ready to accept the idea of central direction at the movement of food supplies.

Lord Boyd Orr's successor was an American from Oregon, Norris Dodd, the candidate of President Truman. A Democrat, successively a pharmacist, rancher, businessman, long and heavily involved in Oregon and national farm politics, he was in 1946 appointed by President Truman as Undersecretary of Agriculture in Washington. He served two years before being chosen as Director General of FAO. Without experience in international affairs, Dodd nevertheless had keen business sense and he brought to FAO its first semblance of rational organization and orderly housekeeping, matters which Orr had neglected. Moreover, he held the Organization together and functioning during the traumatic experience of moving headquarters from Washington to Rome in 1951. This was no mean feat, for the complications involved in moving were staggering. Named by Washington, he was nevertheless poorly supported by Washington, and his position was therefore doubly difficult. Inspiring leadership was out of the question, but at that stage of FAO's life Dodd was probably what FAO needed. But President Eisenhower and his new administration decided in 1953 that Dodd had to go. He went.

Dodd's successor, P. V. Cardon, was in effect named by Ezra Taft Benson, Eisenhower's Secretary of Agriculture. A fellow Mormon from Utah, Cardon had been a professor of agronomy in Montana State Agricultural College, Director of the Utah State Experimental Station, and had had a career in the U.S. Department of Agriculture. Although he was a high grade research administrator, his choice as Director General of FAO at the Conference in November 1953 was a mistake from all points of view, including his own. Courteous, kindly, he was indecisive almost to the point of immobility. Challenged by the Chiefs of the Technical Divisions, who had assumed the prerogatives of semi-independence, savagely and unfairly attacked in the British press, and receiving little support from Washington, Cardon's health failed under the strain of his responsibilities and during a great part of his two years as Director General he was out of circulation. In his absence, however, FAO was run as competently as could be expected by the Deputy Director General, Sir Herbert Broadley of Great Britain. In the summer of

1956 Cardon, ill and under pressure, resigned, and a special session of the FAO Conference was called for September to select a successor.

The circumstances of Dr. Sen's election were not only dramatic, but meaningful, both then and for the future. As might already be suspected from the foregoing accounts, the FAO Conference had been up to then dominated by the United States, Great Britain, and those other advanced countries which had been responsible for the creation of FAO and which contributed most of its resources. It seems scarcely to have been questioned very seriously up to that time that the posts of Director General and Deputy Director General should be American or British.

A different spirit prevailed in the special session of the FAO Conference in 1956. The membership had grown from the original 45 countries to 73, chiefly through the adherence of newly independent underdeveloped countries. And there was serious dissatisfaction with past FAO administration. At the outset, five candidates were nominated. The candidate of the United States was Mr. John H. Davis, a man with a varied career in agriculture, as a teacher in the midwest, as an employee of the U.S. Department of Agriculture, and with private organizations concerned with farmers and farm products. The other candidates were, Mr. R. Cantos-Figuerola of Spain, Mr. J. N. Elizalde of the Philippines, Mr. S. L. Mansholt of the Netherlands, and Mr. B. R. Sen of India. The results of the first ballot taken on the morning of 18 September were unprecedented in FAO: no candidate had received a majority on the first ballot! Mr. Davis had received 33 out of the 73 votes cast and Mr. Sen 19. The other candidates shared the remainder, and two promptly withdrew their names On the second ballot taken the same day, Mr. Davis had 37 votes, Mr. Sen 26, and Mr. Mansholt 11. There was some pretty clear writing on the wall, and by general agreement a further ballot was postponed not to the following day but to the day after that.

There was a big surprise when the Conference met on the morning of 20 September. Mr. Davis withdrew his name from the ballot. He explained that his name had been put forward by the United

States Government because other governments had urged the naming of an American. However, he continued, the United States would support the candidacy of an American only if there was substantial majority support. The earlier ballots had not shown such support and therefore he and his government had decided to withdraw his candidacy. The leader of the U.S. delegation, Mr. Earl Butz, confirmed that although Mr. Davis himself had made the decision, the U.S. Government fully concurred in it. And such was the case. The telephone lines for 36 hours had been hot between Rome, Washington, and London, where Secretary of State Dulles happened to be. Mr. Davis's withdrawal had been cleared with both the Secretary of State and the White House.

In the ensuing ballot, Dr. Sen received 42 votes and Mr. Mansholt 29, and Mr. Sen was declared the new Director General of FAO. In thanking the delegates, Dr Sen paid tribute to the courage and self-denial of Mr. Davis when victory was in sight, and to the generous attitude of the United States. He felt that his election expressed a growing desire on the part of the less-developed areas of the world to play an increasing part in the direction of FAO affairs, and that "only a big nation with a big heart", such as the United States, could have shown such understanding and performed such an outstanding act of renunciation.

That was gracious, frank, and disarming. But it was not the whole story. Dr Sen was the candidate of Great Britain, and in fact a host of the underdeveloped countries supported the American nominee, so there was more to it than a cleavage along developed and underdeveloped lines. United States initiative and idealism had been responsible for the creation of FAO, the United States had generously furnished funds covering a third of the FAO budget, and U.S. leadership had been taken for granted. But U.S. leadership had not for several years been forthcoming. The result was FAO had drifted along while needs and demands upon it mounted. In 1956 it looked as though this situation were going to be perpetuated. Accordingly, feeling grew in developed and underdeveloped countries alike that the United States did not have enough interest in FAO and that a well-qualified Director General from an underdeveloped country might, if aggressive, elicit more support from the United States than an American. The poor showing of the American candidate on two ballots represented a revolt against ineffective administration and a continuation of what had become American control without leadership.

Looking at the situation objectively, there is reason to question whether the United States can provide, or should be expected to provide, vigorous leadership to FAO. Support, yes — but not leadership. In the wide spectrum of U.S. interests FAO occupies a very small band. The U.S. Department of Agriculture has a budget of billions, employs over 80,000 people, and supplies more than $1 billion in surplus food to underdeveloped countries each year under the Food for Peace Program. The U.S. Agency for International Development conducts vast programs of aid to international agriculture. U.S. foreign trade in agricultural products is enormous. It is impossible for FAO to appear as important to the U.S. Government and the American people as it does to the governments and people of the countries who need help. But the U.S. Government is capable of recognizing this, and of giving FAO strong support, even if not leadership.

In introducing his first work program to the FAO Conference in 1957, Dr. Sen said:

> . . . I hope to be able to bring to the service of the Organization and see reflected in its Program of Work my personal knowledge of conditions and needs in those underdeveloped countries where hunger and poverty are still the constant experience of millions of people. While my allegiance is to all nations developed and underdeveloped alike, I can, in a special sense, speak for the millions who are striving out of poverty today in all the world's underveloped regions.

Dr. Sen then proposed an expanded FAO program with a budget to cover it. To its great credit, "the big nation with the big heart" accepted gracefully the reality implicit in Dr. Sen's election and, with reservations which will be mentioned in the next chapter, has given his vigorous administration reasonably good support, certainly much better support than it gave his American predecessors. But the Director General has had to fight for it.

There is an intensity of purpose about B. R. Sen that is surprising in one so bland and urbane in appearance. Whether he is engaged in conversation, or making a public speech, or quietly sitting on a platform listening to others, his eyes betray a preoccupation, and one eventually learns its focus: it is the paradox of hunger and poverty existing in a world of potential plenty. He seems to live with this paradox every waking moment, and those moments are many because he awakes at 4 a.m. and starts working. It is consciousness of this paradox which drives him, makes him impatient of small talk, small actions, and small conceptions — and also impatient of opposition. It is consciousness of this paradox which makes him a forceful Director General of FAO, continually pressing for more resources with which to speed up the process of world agricultural development.

The Director General, a graduate of Oxford, a diplomat with personal experience in many countries, understands and appreciates the ways and the problems of the United States, Great Britain and the other advanced countries. But it does not prevent him from pressing the rich persistently, stubbornly, sometimes infuriatingly, to do more in their own interest for the poor.

Given the qualities of B. R. Sen and the circumstances of his election, it is not surprising that FAO embarked upon a program of expanded services. Eight years later, FAO is a forceful development agency disposing of greatly increased resources, engaged not only in giving advice but also in worldwide operations. All of this, however, is not due to the leadership of the Director General. As it happened, his advent in FAO coincided with a stepping-up of all U.N. development activities and the maturing of world ideas concerning the importance of international development and how to achieve it. As we have seen from previous chapters, the U.N. Special Fund came into existence in early 1959 and FAO became one of its chief executing agents. Also, EPTA and UNICEF funds and projects increased substantially. Development fever became epidemic everywhere. Director General Sen launched his Freedom from Hunger Campaign and the United Nations its Development Decade. More emphasis came to be placed upon national development planning, institution building, indigenous training, and improved government administration. To this general advance of knowledge and method FAO contributed, and it received. The work of the various organs of the United Nations became merged to a greater extent in a planned, integrated U.N. family operation. A senior member of the family with a wide mandate and forceful direction, FAO has played an increasingly active role.

One of the first things Dr. Sen did after he took office was to strengthen FAO's regional organization so as to bring the Organization closer to member countries and better equip it to help them determine their priority needs and reflect those needs back to headquarters. At the time FAO had four Regional Offices (in Cairo, Bangkok, Santiago and Washington), two sub-regional offices (in Mexico City and Rio de Janeiro), and two liaison offices (at United Nations, New York, and in Geneva). However, these were largely skeleton offices, sparsely staffed. The offices had few general officers, few outposted technicians, and very little money for travel within the regions. Several Regional FAO Conferences had taken place, but their relation to policy and program formulation had not been clearly defined. There had been very little planning for systematic FAO servicing of member countries.

The result of these deficiencies was that member countries were frequently unaware of how much FAO was doing and what it was capable of doing. FAO's work made little impact on many national officials and to them the activities of the staff at headquarters seemed remote. Many countries felt there was little opportunity for their recommendations to be considered in the preparation of FAO's Program of Work.

Dr. Sen sought remedies in a number of directions. He widened the scope of the biennial Regional FAO Conferences by having them review regularly past activities in the regions and make recommendations for future programs. He stimulated higher-level representation at those conferences. He took steps to strengthen the staffs of the Regional FAO Offices with additional general officers and technical experts outposted from headquarters with responsibilities for the entire region. He brought about the establishment of a Regional Office for Africa in Accra, and a Liaison Office with the U.N.

Economic Commission for Africa in Addis Ababa. And he secured increased travel funds so as to permit more frequent, scheduled travel within the region and travel between the region and head-quarters. All of these things were done, of course, with the approval of the FAO Conference. However, the regional organization is still not as strong as it might be or as effective as the Director General would like it to be. Two other Sub-Regional Offices have been authorized for Africa, but their location is still a matter of discussion.

A major policy orientation effected by Dr. Sen was of pervasive and long-term significance. FAO had come to be too exclusively technical in its outlook and emphasis, and Dr. Sen called the Organization back to something its founders and the earlier FAO Conferences had recognized but which, along the way, had been almost lost to sight: it was that FAO technical activities have significance only because they serve a human purpose, and are justifiable only in so far as they serve human welfare. People will never use or benefit from improved technology unless they are able to grasp its meaning in human terms. Within the compass of FAO's mandate, Dr. Sen declared, the central focus should be the fuller growth of the human being, alone, in the family, and as a member of a larger social group.

The implications of this shift in focus were broad, and Dr. Sen pointed them out in his first work message to the FAO Conference in November 1957. He proposed that the Organization equip itself to give more help to member countries in the following fields:

Building agricultural institutions and services, especially extension services necessary to support agricultural enterprises.

Land reform and land settlement.

Farm credit and agricultural investment.

Agricultural education, including the training of rural youth.

Nutrition and home economics.

Rural communication and overall rural community development.

And agricultural development planning as part of general pro-grams of economic planning, with attention to all aspects of rural welfare.

Dr. Sen has been able to go some way towards achieving his purposes by means of internal personnel increases and organization changes, through emphasis in FAO studies and meetings, by helping member countries with their planning, and by advising governments to ask EPTA for the right kinds of technical specialists to come and help them. However, it was only when the U.N. Special Fund came into existence that FAO was able to make dramatic headway in the fields mentioned above.

The most important accomplishment of Dr. Sen's administration has been the transformation of FAO from a technical advisory organization into a development agency. When he took charge, the various technical and economic divisions of FAO were operating semi-independently rendering advice and assistance to governments as requested, without much attention to whether the government had any kind of plan for the best use of their limited resources. Most of them did not have a plan, had had little experience with planning, and lacked competent planners. The Regular Program of studies, conferences and technical meetings, the techical assistance program, the fellowship program, FAO/UNICEF projects — all the different resources and operating arms of FAO were helping governments semi-independently, and all too often their activities were un-coordinated.

The new Director General took the position that FAO should help countries and regional groups of countries survey their resources, plan their agricultural growth as part of an overall economic development program, and in the light of facts determine their priority needs. All of the operating arms of FAO would be brought to bear upon this work, and once priority needs were determined, would concentrate upon helping meet those needs. In his first work program he emphasized a planned, regional approach to the problems of the countries bordering on the Mediterranean and asked the Conference for funds to intensify surveys essential to planned improvement. Two years later, he instituted a similar approach to the problems of Africa. The FAO Conference of 1961 granted him limited funds in the FAO budget for direct technical assistance to countries seeking help in agricultural planning and for a special

Africa educational program. Conferences, meetings, fellowships, technical assistance — all began to emphasize and support planning. FAO's new philosophy was set forth in a report entitled "Forward Appraisal of FAO Programs, 1959–64", submitted in 1959 to the U.N. Economic and Social Council. It is a thoughtful document, and one that has been followed in the years since with surprising precision.

During 1957 and 1958 the Director General also altered FAO's organizational structure in order to increase the capacity of the technical and economic divisions for team operations, to bring them under the effective guidance and control of senior policy officers reporting to the Director General, and better focus the efforts of the Organization on the priority needs of governments. Before this, chiefs of technical divisions had been operating, as someone has said, as feudal barons, paying public homage to the Administration, but in fact operating independently in their domains. The reorganization improved this situation considerably, but old habits die hard.

Keeping a trained eye on FAO's complex operations is Oris Vernon Wells, Deputy Director General. Mr. Wells is an American, who from 1946 to 1954 was Chief of the Bureau of Agricultural Economics in the U.S. Department of Agriculture, and from 1954 to 1961 Administrator of the Department's Agricultural Marketing Service. Mr. Wells has been in his new post for only two years, but for the two years preceding he had been an Assistant Director General in FAO. Even when he came to FAO in 1961 he was no stranger to the Organization, having served as adviser on U.S. delegations to six FAO Conferences and, over the years, on many FAO Committees, including the Program Committee. Mr. Wells seems completely at home in FAO and is the object of universal respect. He makes it his job to know every detail about the Organization and its operations, his memory is favored by total recall, and his talents at administration are marked. He advises the Director General on policy, but subject to the plans and decisions and wishes of the captain, he is the man on the bridge who runs the ship of FAO.

A final but most important innovation of Dr. Sen needs mention here, although it will be treated in some detail later. Not long after he became Director General, Dr. Sen began to think about the need for a continuous, worldwide campaign which would publicize the facts of hunger and malnutrition, arouse public support for national and U.N. efforts to increase food supplies, and stimulate vast private activities directed towards the abolition of those twin evils which need no longer exist in the world. Thus, he worked out a plan for a Freedom from Hunger Campaign. His plan, approved by the FAO Conference, the U.N. Economic and Social Council, and in 1960 by the U.N. General Assembly, was launched and is directed from FAO headquarters in Rome. Now in its fifth year, the Freedom from Hunger Campaign has been highly successful in many countries, less so in others. Substantial accomplishments are already to its credit, and its potential is great, for hunger will never disappear from the earth unless all people in all nations are enlisted in the battle against it.

The Director General of FAO proposes, but the FAO Conference disposes. Let us now take a brief look at the FAO Conference and the biennial battle of the budget.

CHAPTER 3

THE CONFERENCE,
AND BATTLE OF THE BUDGET

THAT corporate entity, that family reunion, that endless Sahara of meetings, that frantic mutual pursuit of visiting officials and FAO staff, that controlling body known as the FAO Conference assembles for several weeks once each two years, usually in November. If it met any oftener, FAO operations, like Rome traffic, would soon approach a final, monumental, inextricable jam. The official conference, consisting of one delegate from each member country, meets to review the work of FAO, determine its future policies and programs, vote its budget, and once each 4 years elect a Director General. Each official delegate, however, is accompanied by a sizeable group of alternates, advisers, and technical specialists ranging in number from two to sixteen or more. Around the official conference, in offices, corridors, bars, restaurants, hotel rooms, swirls the unofficial conference where FAO staff and visiting officials from all over the world get to know each other, talk over problems and transact business.

When the Twelfth Biennial FAO Conference opened in Rome on the brilliant morning of 16 November 1963, the flags of 104 members and associate members fluttered in the breeze in a long row along the Viale Aventino. The arriving delegations swept purposefully through the entrance doors of the Conference building, and consciously ignoring the camera flashlights, mounted three steps to the reception lobby where they plunged into a sea of smiles and outstretched hands. There seemed to be few strangers. For most of them it was a familiar homecoming. In time they made their way to the large main conference hall on the third floor where, waylaid by friends on every hand, they searched for their allotted spaces. Slowly, confusion yielded and the Director General called the assembly to order. The venerable and gracious Ambassador E. Shiroshi Nasu of Japan was, according to pre-arrangement by the Council, promptly elected Chairman of the Conference. After brief welcoming remarks, the Ambassador called on Director General Sen to give his opening address. The Conference was under way.

Nearly 3 weeks later, near the end of the Conference, eight new flags were hoisted along the Viale Aventino, bringing the total to 106 members and 6 associate members. Those in the sparse group attending the ceremony were markedly less ebullient than they had been upon arrival. Eyes had receded, words and smiles had become somewhat mechanical. There was good reason. The delegates and FAO staff had been through a mill.

For the FAO staff and many of the delegates, the November meeting of the Conference itself was merely the culmination of a long process of budget and program preparation and scrutiny begun shortly after the close of the previous Conference 2 years earlier. In the spring of 1962 the Program and Finance Committees of the FAO Council had considered the work and program and had reported to the twenty-seven member Council which had met in June to thresh FAO affairs and give guidance to the Director General. During 1962 five Regional Conferences had taken place — in Tel Amara, Lebanon, Rio de Janeiro, Tunis, Kuala Lumpur, and Lisbon. Each had reviewed FAO's work and each had made recommendations for future programs. By March 1963 the Director General's proposed Program of Work and Budget, a document thick, elaborate and detailed, had been distributed to member countries. During the ensuing months the Council's Standing Committee had studied the document, reported to the Council, and the Council meeting in a heated 9-day session in June 1963 had turned the Director General's program and budget inside out, and prepared a report and recommendations for the Conference.

During the summer and early fall of 1963 Rome headquarters had prepared and distributed to all member countries more than sixty special studies analyzing in detail each question that might conceivably come before the Conference. And by September, the annual publication, *The State of Food and Agriculture*, prepared under the

direction of the veteran P. G. H. Barter, Chief of FAO's Economic
Analysis Division, had been completed and distributed to members.
When the chief delegates arrived for the opening of the Conference
on 16 November advance members of their delegations had already
been hard at work for 2 weeks in six Technical Committees — covering agriculture, forestry, fisheries, nutrition, and information and
publications — where every buried body had been exhumed, every
living body on the FAO payroll figuratively stripped and searched in
three languages, and every dollar of proposed expenditure squeezed
until the eagle screamed.

After the opening Plenary Session and the address of the Director
General, four main shows, with every member represented or entitled
to be represented, went on simultaneously. In the main Conference
hall the Ministers of Agriculture or other chief delegates delivered
their fixed speeches, one after another for nearly two weeks, with a
monotony only occasionally relieved by inspiration or eloquence.
Meanwhile, the Conference work was carried on in three separate
Commissions. In one, the state of food and agriculture in general
was considered; in a second, legal and administrative matters were
debated; and in a third the Director General's Program of Work and
Budget underwent still another dissection, this time with the aid of
the reports of the Technical Committees. In the end, all three
Commissions voted on all relevant matters and reported to the
Plenary Session where, with the exception of a few questions such
as the final budget figure, consideration was perfunctory and final
approvals speedy.

In any well-run international conference the delegates know fairly
well in advance what is going to happen. FAO Conferences are
well run. The congeries of meetings is well scheduled, the translation services work well, reports and verbatim proceedings, by the
ton and in three languages, usually appear when and where they
should. And what everybody expects to happen to the main issues
before the Conference usually happens.

An objective observer can only wonder, then, whether such
elaborate, time-consuming preparation, such a debilitating endur-
ance contest, is really necessary. The entire FAO budget could be

supported without hardship by a single, medium-sized advanced country. It is in fact divided among 106 countries varying from the large and rich to the small and poor. The individual program and budget items are so numerous, involve such small sums, and are examined with such care so many times at so many levels, and yet frequently arouse such high feelings, that the question recurs often: is all this scrutiny necessary? Late one afternoon in the third weary week of the Conference, after listening to representatives from a dozen African and Asian countries give their views on the phrasing of a resolution instructing the Director General to do something about Quelea quelea birds and water hyacinths, I decided it was *not* really necessary.

But I was, of course, wrong. Those pestiferous birds that eat the crops and those water hyacinths that spread like a plague and clog irrigation canals mean, to many people, hunger. And whether or not the views of twelve countries are needed to draft a simple resolution, FAO is their organization and it is important that its members be concerned about its details. At meetings at all levels where program and budget are dissected, officials of differing degrees of responsibility from ministries of agriculture all over the world are learning about their own problems, about problems of other countries, about what FAO can do to help them, and about what they can do for FAO. In the process they are acquiring confidence and responsibility. And just as often as the question arose as to whether the complex procedure of program and budget making was really necessary, it was answered. Yes, definitely.

FAO's program, worked out so laboriously, necessarily finds expression in the budget. Fixing the budget figure is one of the chief functions of the Conference and, as is the case with institutional budgets everywhere and at all times, the figure involves a battle. But FAO's battle of the budget is not a fierce fray that occurs only at the Conference. It is a continuous engagement with frequent skirmishes, leading inevitably toward the biennial conference struggle and ending in a vote which establishes a position for two years.

Certain facts determine the nature of FAO's battle of the budget, and its outcome.

Member countries support the budget according to a scale of contributions worked out by the United Nations, based upon capacity to pay as indicated by their average national incomes over a period of years. No single member, however, is assessed at more than one-third of the total, and none less than 0.04 per cent. Except for this arbitrary cut-off, which is the rule in the United Nations and all U.N. agencies, the United States, whose national income is around half of the world total, would pay approximately half of the FAO budget. As it is, however, the United States pays 32 per cent, the United Kingdom 10 per cent, and France and the Federal Republic of Germany each slightly less than 8 per cent. Ten developed countries together pay 73 per cent. Sixteen countries combined pay 87 per cent.

The FAO budget, which until 1959 was voted by a simple majority, has since then required two-thirds for approval. Inasmuch as the chief purpose of FAO, as it has grown over the years, is to serve as a U.N. agency aiding the development of the poorer countries, it is natural and expected that these should receive far more in benefits from FAO than they contribute. But deep-seated trouble stems from the fact that they are in such an overwhelming majority in FAO that they can and do vote budgets which may be opposed by the ten countries who pay nearly three-quarters of it or twenty who pay 90 per cent of it.

At some future stage of international organization and outlook this may not cause much trouble. It perhaps should not do so now, but it does. Within the boundaries of most sovereign states the well-to-do are taxed for the benefit of those less fortunate, the poor receive far more from the government than they contribute, and the masses have the franchise and vote the taxes. Moreover, this is generally recognized by most citizens, rich, middle class and poor alike, as being in their best interests. But the international community has not yet reached that stage. The members of FAO are sovereign states, and paying assessments voted by a majority of other sovereign states goes against the grain.

There is, however, more to their attitudes than national reluctance to pay for a budget voted by other countries who receive most of the benefits, and more than parsimony. Most of the countries who seek to cut the Director General's budget are democracies where elected bodies, as a matter of tradition, constitution, and normal housekeeping, examine and cut budgets proposed by the Executive. They find in their own national budgets what they regard as "fat" to be cut out, unnecessary operations and overlaps that can be eliminated. And on principle they consider that cutting back on figures proposed by the Executive is a necessary way of keeping the organization lean and efficient. The attitude has deep roots, and it is reflected in the positions which the governments of the developed countries take toward the FAO budget. But aside from attitudes, the officials who determine their governments' national contribution to the FAO budget are not free agents. Watchdogs of their own national budgets are looking over their shoulders and must be satisfied. The FAO contribution must go into national budgets whose level is always a matter of close scrutiny, heartburn and controversy, and must compete with thousands of other financial claims. There is obviously much more than thriftiness, short-sightedness or caprice which prompts the governments of developed countries to exercise a restraining hand on the FAO budget.

The attitude of the United States toward any budget proposed by the Director General bears great weight. The views of the richest country in the world, the country with the most prosperous agriculture and the most advanced agricultural technology, the country which supplies a third of FAO's funds, are automatically important. The U.S. Government has always paid close attention to FAO finances. However, the U.S. Congress, against the wishes of the Administration, for many years imposed an absolute ceiling on the U.S. contribution as a condition to U.S. initial membership. In the early years when FAO was largely a headquarters-bound technical organization, this was no great handicap, and there were several years when it did not spend all the money budgeted. During the 1950's, as FAO's world responsibilities grew, the U.S. Congress raised the ceiling, then in 1960 removed it altogether. But regardless of the ceiling imposed by Congress, the United States, over the years, has generally sought both overtly and behind the scenes, to restrain the expansion of the budget, no matter what increase was proposed, and on several occasions it has openly and strongly opposed the Director General's proposals. For example, it opposed the increases proposed in 1955 by the American Director General, Mr. Cardon, and it opposed some of the budget proposals of Director General Sen in 1961 and 1963.

Except for the fact that its position bears greater weight, there is no reason to single out the United States among the countries which try to limit expansion of FAO's budget. Great Britain, France, Germany, Italy, Canada, Australia — in fact most of the major contributors, all developed countries — have as a rule taken positions similar to that of the United States. They have not opposed FAO expansion, but they have usually sought to reduce the degree of expansion proposed by the Director General.

Most FAO budgets are the result of off-stage soundings, discussions, and adjustment involving the Director General and officials of the leading member countries. The process is continuous, and extends up to the final conference vote on the budget level. But it did not function well in 1961 or 1963.

As we have seen in the preceding chapter, the first budget which Director General Sen in November 1957 proposed to the FAO Conference for the 2 years 1958 and 1959 covered a more vigorous expanded program and represented a substantial increase over the preceding budget. It was nevertheless in the end supported unanimously by the Conference after only token criticism of specific items. In November 1959 the Director General proposed only a 12 per cent increase for 1960 and 1961, of which two-thirds was for "mandatory" adjustments in salary scales, allowances, and other commitments. This was in effect a standstill budget for what Dr. Sen described as a period of "consolidation". There was little increase in program. Again, the Conference approved with only normal complaints. The story, however, was different in 1961. Dr. Sen proposed for 1962/63 a 46 per cent increase in the FAO budget which was openly, strongly, even bitterly opposed up until the final vote by the United States and most of the other developed countries. In the end, however, it being clear that the underdeveloped countries had the votes and were going to approve the budget level proposed by the Director General, the "opposition" joined to support it, and no vote was recorded against it. Though the percentage increase was large, we are not talking about astronomical sums here: the increase raised the annual FAO expenditure from $10.8 million to $15.6 million for a world organization!

In retrospect, it is difficult to see how any competent FAO Chief Executive could have failed in 1961 to propose a very large increase in the budget even though he knew it would be to some degree opposed by the leading contributors. The 1960–1 budget having been in effect "standstill", FAO was operating at a budget level fixed 4 years earlier. And during those four years the world had moved far and fast. Twenty-two newly independent, underdeveloped countries, most of them in Africa, had acquired membership by the end of the 1961 Conference; two more had become associate members; and more than half a dozen others were expected to apply for membership before the end of 1963. They needed help in a hurry if the heady wine of independence were not to yield to chaos as colonial administrators, technicians, businessmen and foreign settlers withdrew.

But apart from the drastic alteration of the map of the world by the emergence of new countries, the entire underdeveloped world had been swept by hope and expectation for rapid economic and social improvement. Moreover, the consequences of rapid population growth had begun to be realized. "Development fever" raged, and pressures multiplied upon the United Nations for more help in building toward self-sustaining economic growth. The United Nations had declared the 1960's to be a Development Decade in which all underdeveloped countries were to achieve an annual economic growth rate of 5 per cent. FAO's Freedom from Hunger Campaign had been launched, had caught on, and needed fuel. The U.N. Special Fund had been created and was in full swing, the U.N. Technical Assistance Program had been enlarged, and UNICEF resources had nearly doubled. These had transformed FAO into a major operating agency, but they provided funds mostly for specific projects and had failed by far to cover the additional costs of drawing up hundreds of projects and back-stopping them. FAO field operations had increased four-fold since 1959. Eighty per cent of the people in the poorer countries of the world depended directly upon agriculture for their livelihood, and the importance of improved agriculture to overall economic development had been increasingly realized. More help for development planning had become a necessity if the resources of developing countries were to be effectively used.

All of these pressures, accumulated over four years, had piled up on the doorstep of Director General Sen by November 1961. Also, FAO needed $2 million to cover nominal needs which were accepted by all as "mandatory" in a properly functioning institution. Under these circumstances, Director General Sen asked the membership of nearly 100 countries to supply, together, an additional $5 million a year to meet FAO's vastly increased responsibilities and opportunities. The Conference in the end agreed, but scars remained, and positions began to be taken on the budget level for 1964–65.

The pressures, mentioned above, which operated on FAO in 1961 had not lessened when the budget for 1964–65 was in preparation. On the contrary, they had very considerably increased. The greater FAO services made possible by the 1962–63 budget had created a demand for still more. It was obvious that most of the countries of Asia, Africa, and Latin America were not on the road to achieving the goals of the U.N. Development Decade. An ominous note had been added by a downturn in *per capita* food production in Asia. Exploding population was bearing more heavily on food supply. The ebullience generated by independence in three dozen countries had given way to hard realities of administration and making a national living. The FAO Regular Program staff was being pressed harder as Special Fund and UNICEF projects executed by or in conjunction with FAO grew geometrically. Thus, the Director General in 1963 asked for a further 25 per cent increase in funds for 1964 and 1965. This meant that the budget figure for the *two years* would rise from $31,185,000 to $38,973,000, and would provide increased resources of nearly $4 million each year. One quarter of

F

the increase, however, was generally agreed to be "mandatory", so that only $3 million a year was for program expansion.

Following the recommendations of the Program Committee, the Director General urged that the increased funds be used chiefly to intensify activity and services to governments in four fields: planning for more effective use of scarce resources; education and training, institution building, and improvement of essential government services to agriculture; improving diet, with emphasis on raising and consuming high protein foods; and increasing food supplies by reducing losses occurring in storage, processing and marketing.

The United States had made it plain during 1962 that it would not support an increase in the 1964–65 budget of more than 12 to 15 per cent, and other leading contributors had expressed similar views. At the June 1963 session of the FAO Council, the U.S. representative repeated his government's position, and went farther to suggest specific reductions in individual items totalling $2,332,050. This would have brought the budget increase near the 15 per cent which, he declared, was the maximum his government would support. He was promptly backed by the representatives of Austria, Australia, Belgium, Ireland, the United Kingdom, France, Italy, Denmark and Pakistan. The represenatives of Indonesia, Cuba, Morocco, India, Lebanon and the United Arab Republic supported the budget level proposed by the Director General. It was a stormy session. The heavy contributors called for streamlining, eliminating "dead wood", and maintained their position for a maximum 15 per cent increase. Dr. Sen, exasperated, exclaimed:

> We are fighting a big war to save millions of lives. If we are to do that then we should not think only in terms of percentages. When you have a war, do you think of your normal national budget or do you put in whatever is needed to win the war? Unless members of the Council and member nations realize we are fighting a war then all this unrealistic discussion will go on. . . . At the World Food Congress it was made clear that we must try to ensure the development of food production three to fourfold in the developing regions of the world. Most of these regions depend on FAO for guidance or technical matters. Will FAO be able to meet the demands of these nations if FAO is restricted in developing its program of work in this way?

The FAO Conference which assembled in Rome on 16 November 1963 was not, after it got down to business, a happy one. In fact, it was one of the two most troubled in the history of the Organization. The United States had made the mistake (one which there is reason to believe is regretted and will not be repeated) of taking a fixed position on the percentage by which the budget could be enlarged and of reinforcing it in advance with recommendations for specific cuts. In the technical committees and commissions, day after day for three weeks the U.S. delegates were obliged, obviously upon instructions, to be negative, insistent upon cuts. They never made a constructive suggestion. And they were monotonously outvoted. The effect was, to say the least, deplorable. The amount of money involved in the showdown, the amount in the budget for which the U.S. delegation for 3 weeks fought and bled was about $2 million for 2 years, of which the U.S. share would have been less than a third, about $300,000 a year. For this, the most powerful and the most generous nation on earth deployed enormous pressures on member countries. For this, a great country risked contempt in an international forum. In reaction, the Director General encouraged resistance, earning still further criticism from the "opposition".

The chief U.S. proposals for cuts would have eliminated all funds for increased FAO staff to cope with the burgeoning UNICEF program and would have prevented strengthening of the FAO Regional staff with an additional twenty-three outposted technical officers. The United States, and the "opposition" generally, insisted that UNICEF should pay FAO's headquarters costs in connection with joint programs. The principle involved was that any U.N. agency originating a project should pay all its costs, but it had been abandoned years before in connection with joint UNICEF/World Health Organization projects, and UNICEF was objecting strongly to a continued payment of subsidy to FAO. It was not a principle to die for in any case as the same countries would in the end, regardless of to which agency, pay the same amount of money for the UNICEF program.

As for strengthening the Regional FAO offices, the "opposition" wanted a study of the need, which would have meant a 2-year delay.

The technical officers outposted to the regions are FAO circuit riders who carry FAO competence to the countries where it is most needed, press government departments to do what they should be doing, advise them on how to do it, and give them or help them get whatever assistance they need. When one is at FAO headquarters in Rome, one wonders what on earth the Regional Offices are doing; and when he is in the field, he wonders what headquarters finds to do. I visited four of the five FAO Regional Offices, and it seemed to me that some of the most effective cutting edges of FAO are there.

Out in front as leader of the opposition to the full scope of the Director General's budget, the United States was nevertheless supported all along the line by virtually every developed country. This time, unlike its yielding in the previous conference, the opposition held its position to the end. A budget close to the Director General's original proposal was approved by more than a two-thirds majority. But twenty-seven countries who support 82 per cent of the budget voted against it. The twenty-seven included only five of the "have not" countries.

A vote of this kind reflects a problem of the most profound importance, not only for FAO but for several of the U.N. agencies, and there is no prospect for an early or easy solution to it. So long as FAO was a fairly static technical agency with a small budget the problem could be glossed over. But now that FAO is a major development agency with a substantial and growing budget — and perhaps more important, with increasing demands upon it and greater opportunities for world service — the problem cannot be ignored. The internationalism of the advanced countries of the world, the contributors, and the wisdom, judgement and restraint of the receivers are going to be put to a real test.

It is ironical that the trouble should arise out of the success, not failure, of the U.N. institutions they created. Those institutions have performed so well that their services, when available on equal terms, are preferred to bilateral aid. They have so succeeded in attracting the loyalty and confidence of the underdeveloped countries and in laying the foundations for technical competence and hopes for progress that the beginnings of an international order are visible.

If at this point the poorer countries become reckless, and if the richer should call a halt to the growth of the international institutions they took the lead in creating, a historical tragedy would be in the making.

Not only do the developing countries regard the U.N. agencies as "theirs" and therefore more comfortable to deal with (even though they know very well where most of the money comes from), but the U.N. agencies are frequently better equipped to help them. In a conversation with me, Hassan Abdallah, Director of Foreign Relations of the Ministry of Agriculture in Cairo, was most articulate:

> In many cases we prefer to approach U.N. agencies for help because from them we have the experts and experience of the whole world to draw on. Frequently we need the experience of specialists from countries which have conditions similar to ours, or which have solved problems similar to ours. For example, we asked for experts from India to help us with our agricultural and fisheries statistics, not only because India is advanced in statistical sampling techniques, but because India and Egypt have similar social and economic conditions, whereas conditions, say, in the United States, are far different from ours. Also, all experts helping us with our tile drainage problems are from Holland, because that country, which has been battling the sea for centuries, has acquired superior experience in drainage. So you can see why it is that of the 80 FAO experts who have served in this country, 24 came from the United States, 15 from the Netherlands, six from the United Kingdom, six from India, five from Canada, five from Germany, four from Switzerland, two from Denmark and one each from Lebanon, Philippines, France, Norway, U.S.S.R. and Poland.
>
> Through FAO we have a whole world to choose from not only in selecting experts, but also in getting the kind of equipment we need. For example, we got a fishing boat from Norway; we got small agricultural implements from Japan and Holland where agricultural holdings are much nearer to ours in size than in the United States; and we got breeding fish from Thailand which we especially needed.
>
> The same is true of fellowships. We have been able to send trainees to study cotton breeding in the United States, vegetable and fruit packing in Spain and the Canary Islands, rice production in Japan, sericulture in Italy, and fish culture in Indonesia. Actually, more of our fellowship trainees have gone to the Netherlands than to any other country. We have sent trainees under fellowships to 26 different countries where they could get the specialized kind of training adapted to our needs, and many of these were underdeveloped countries. My country also furnishes a great deal of training and technical assistance to other countries, especially in this region.

Hassan Abdallah is so impressed by FAO assistance that he has written a lengthy book on the subject. It is published in Arabic and its title, translated into English, is *The UAR and FAO*.

That the developing countries obviously have an interest in higher U.N. agency budgets is clear. But they also have an interest in appreciating the dilemma of the advanced countries, major contributors to the budgets of the U.N. agencies. Being in a minority, the leading contributors are *technically* in a position where they can at some future time be assessed by the majority to a point of hardship. If they do not watch the U.N. budgets closely, if they do not exercise a restraining hand, the situation might get out of control. It seems to be fear of future recklessness at least as much as present thrift that prompts the "haves" to seek, consistently, to restrain the budget growth of U.N. agencies.

However, it is extremely difficult for the developing countries, or any objective observer, to take seriously any present hardship claims. Any one of several major contributors, certainly the United States, could carry the *entire* FAO 1964–65 budget increase simply by reducing the amount it spends on bilateral aid in a single country.

Part of the solution to the dilemma lies in official and public acceptance of several facts. One is that U.N. agencies can do many though not all jobs better than bilateral aid programs. Another is that when they can do a job with equal competence they are preferred by the underdeveloped countries, for they consider that the U.N. agencies are *their* instruments and that when they ask them for help they are not going outside the family. Still another is that aid through U.N. agencies wins more friends for the contributing countries, if that is an objective, than bilateral aid. These facts suggest a more generous attitude toward expansion of the budgets of FAO and the other U.N. agencies, and a conscious effort to channel money through them even if it must be at the expense of bilateral aid programs. It also suggests that the developing countries make greater efforts to appreciate the awkward position in which the leading contributors to the budgets of U.N. agencies frequently find themselves.

Even without changing public attitudes, a great deal would be gained if the advanced countries were to consider the work, the needs, and the opportunities of FAO at a higher level and in greater perspective. The officials in member countries who deal with FAO affairs are few and most of them operate at medium levels. They constitute the FAO family, and they are remarkably possessive about the Organization, and ingrown. They are often so close to operations that they fail to see the woods for the trees. Because they examine the small details, because they know of technical meetings or projects that have been failures, because they are aware that this or that division chief is ambitious and tends to promote his speciality unwarrantedly, they are inclined to magnify cases of inefficiency and to see pounds of institutional fat that can be cut off where there may be ounces. FAO's program is of such a character that the margin for fat or waste in any particular project or operation is small indeed. Concentration upon details is useful, but it desperately needs to be balanced by statesmanship, by a conception of the institution's work as a whole, by awareness of the harsh realities outlined earlier in this book.

This statesmanship, this awareness, these larger views, are too seldom reflected upon FAO by the leading contributing countries. Their Ministers of Agriculture frequently attend briefly the opening sessions of the FAO Conference and sometimes make statesman-like speeches. At home in their countries there is no dearth of statesmanship at the higher levels. But too seldom does it carry through to day by day operations of their staffs.

The chief executive of any operating U.N. agency is only an agent of member countries. And no matter who he may be he is put in an awkward and difficult position if he is obliged to supply most of the statesmanship to the world organization which he leads. This should be provided in large part by the leading member countries. But far too little of it has been forthcoming. This being the case, a good executive must stand out in front, expose himself to criticism, point to facts, dangers, opportunities, and ask insistently for the support of a progressive program.

One of the final acts of the Twelfth Biennial FAO Conference was to re-elect B. R. Sen for a third 4-year term as Director General. There were no other nominees.

PART IV

New Approaches

CHAPTER I

THE MEDITERRANEAN

FLYING from Lisbon to Rabat, capital of Morocco, my plane proceeded southeast, skirting the coast of Spain as far as Gibraltar, and then turned abruptly south. From 20,000 feet, the formidable rock guarding the thirty mile entrance to the Mediterranean looked small and innocent. Hardly had I sighted it than I was over the Rif mountains of Northern Morocco. Famous in history as the home of the Berbers, stronghold of pirate and rebel, the Rif are neither especially high nor outstandingly rugged as mountains go. But they are difficult of access, and the few roads penetrating them are of recent construction. The Rif extend eastward until they join the Middle Atlas chain, but in western Morocco they extend southward only about 75 miles before yielding suddenly to the broad valleys and plains of the Rharb and the Sebou Basin, the most prosperous and promising agricultural area in the whole of Morocco.

My first sight of the valleys and plains south of the Rif puzzled me. They were not green, as were the foothills, but the color of lead, looking as though they had been covered with lava which, spilling from some unseen volcano, had followed the river beds, overflowed their banks and covered the surrounding land. When I reached Rabat a few minutes later I learned that what I had seen was not lava but clay and silt from the eroded and deforested Rif mountains, deposited by the Sebou River and its tributaries during the floods which had occurred 2 months earlier. Both those floods had been mild, I was told, compared with the disaster of 1960 when flood waters had covered half a million acres.

In the days following I visited the Rif, the Rharb and the Sebou Basin at greater length on the ground. I discovered that I had already seen from the air the geography of poverty, and of a planned national development effort being undertaken by the Government of Morocco with the help of FAO and the U.N. Special Fund.

Conditions in the Rif and the Rharb illustrate vividly the need for a planned approach to national development. Let us begin with the Rif.

More than mud flows from those Rif mountains to inundate the valleys and plains and cities below. People flow from them too, poor people, and discontent, and political instability. The people of the Rif, living almost within sight of the Mediterranean, are not much better off than the poorest, most backward, least educated in the world, and they are increasing rapidly in an unproductive rural area already densely populated. The present Rif population of 1,200,000 is expected to double in 25 years. Unemployed most of the year, they line the village streets and watch the world go by with listless, apathetic eyes; and increasingly they drift south and add to the poverty and restlessness on the fringes of the cities. Without strong political loyalties they were during the 1920's and 1930's frequently in rebellion against French or Spanish authority and at the same time their supply of recruits to the French and Spanish armies was an important economic prop and a palliative for unemployment. With peace and the unification of French and Spanish Morocco, both prop and palliative are gone. It is not without significance that the only rebellion against the authority of the monarchy since independence occurred in the Rif.

Someone has said that the decline of Mediterranean civilization is attributable to the goat, and while this may be a simplification, there is no question that from one end of the Mediterranean to the other, uncontrolled destruction by those free-ranging, insensitive beasts has been an important cause of deforestation and of consequent erosion, floods and poverty. Scrawny, yielding little in milk, meat, or wool, almost worthless, they attack hillsides and eat every green thing, including grass, shrubs, the leaves and bark of older trees, the shoots of new trees. The Rif is full of goats. Because of uncontrolled habits of these creatures, and because of wasteful cutting and burning of trees, hillsides have become bare, and during torrential rains have eroded. There has been no attempt at reforestation or other erosion control by building terraces or earth "banquettes". Untended soils divided into small plots have become unproductive almost to the point of sterility. Ancient olive trees, neglected and unreplaced, yield little. Thus, ignorance has bred extreme poverty, and both together have bred a mentality suspicious of change. Tens of thousands of women of the Rif do not even know how to use a needle and thread, as is evident from the appearance of the ragged, unmended clothes of men and children.

The Rif mountains are visited at certain seasons by torrential rains whose waters, charged with Rif soil, sweep uncontrolled down into the valleys and plains to the south in the Sebou Basin and deposit there their disastrous cargo. The increasing frequency of these floods is one of the main reasons why the Government of Morocco is now eager to do something about the Rif.

The Sebou River originates in the Atlas mountains nearly a hundred miles southeast of Fez and is joined on its way to the sea at Khenitra by many tributaries, chief of which is the Ouerrha River which drains the southern Rif. The Sebou and the Ouerrha can, each by itself, become violent and destructive following torrential rains. But when their turbulences join forces in the plain north of Sidi Kacem disaster is inevitable.

The road north from Fez to Taounate crosses the Ouerrha and runs alongside of it for a distance. When I traveled it, the main bridge had been destroyed by the floods of 2 months earlier, the road was washed out in many places, and at a number of points the course of the river had changed. Villages, partly destroyed, hung precariously on undermined banks. Some had disappeared. Several days later I drove through the Rharb plains farther to the west near the junction of the Sebou and the Ouerrha. Most of the roads had been cleared of silt as though by a snowplow, and we drove between high banks of mud lining the roads. Vast fields of wheat and beans, orange groves, all vegetation was suffocated under a foot or two of the disgusting, dead mud. Railway lines were covered, trestles washed out, irrigation works destroyed. It was an appalling sight.

The land of the Sebou Basin is normally the most fertile, the most productive, and the most promising in Morocco. The area contains many of the country's larger cities, including Fez and Meknes, and the beginnings of industry. Most of the large French-owned farms, many of them models of efficiency, are in the basin. Some of these, which were originally seized by the French and handed over to French owners, have been expropriated and are being divided up. Others, bought by French owners, and farmed by them, have been left untouched. However, the basin as a whole is seriously under-developed. If there is not flood, there is often drought, and the land is for a large part of the year too wet or too dry and caked to work. There is plenty of rainfall, but it is capricious, uncontrolled, and unstored. The native farmers are mostly innocent of knowledge of irrigation, crop diversification, fertilizers or any modern method. There are few government services to agriculture, poor marketing facilities, almost no local industries to serve as outlets for agricultural products. It is pathetic to see a beautiful land which has so much, and yet which yields so little.

The Rif and the Sebou Basin are only two of the seven regions of Morocco, each of which has different characteristics and different problems. Of the remaining I shall mention only the vast plains which extend some 200 miles south of Casablanca between the ocean and the Atlas mountains. Seen in February these are green and beautiful, but later in the year, after an initial crop, they become dry and brown. Grain is grown in the northern part, but as the steppes extend south they become fit largely for pasturage. The farms are neat, the farm dwellings have an air of self-respect. But here again, ignorance of modern methods — seed selection, dry farming, windbreaks, water conservation, range management, livestock development, growing fodder for feeding to cows, sheep and goats during the dry season — ignorance keeps people poor who do not need to be poor. The livestock die or become skin and bones during the dry season.

Morocco is one of the fairest lands on earth to look upon. One cannot help but wonder instinctively, over and over again, why it is not one of the most prosperous countries in the world. But then, one remembers and knows why. It is the ignorance of millennia. The French, who came only in this century, built a splended network of modern roads and communications. They exploited the minerals and built handsome modern cities alongside the native.

The farm lands of which they took possession and worked were made productive. The European segment of the economy of the country was aligned to France, and markets were assured. But the European economy coexisted alongside the native with scarcely any intermingling. The French failed to modernize native agriculture or to make any impact whatever on the fellahin, who continued to farm as he had done for centuries. Just as in the cities the modern European sections ignore and are completely apart from the adjacent native sections, so in the country the modern French farms coexist with neighboring rural backwardness unchanged for centuries.

This was the situation which existed when Morocco became independent in March 1956, and King Mohammed V faced the problem of beginning the building of a modern Moroccan state. His problem would have been far worse had not nearly 20,000 Frenchmen remained in administrative posts, had not the United States poured $405 million into the country in aid during 1957–63, and had not the personnel of three large American air bases, now removed, spend further tens of millions of dollars in the country. But all of this was temporary, and regarded as such. How to start building for economic viability when so many of the ingredients were lacking?

This was only the Moroccan version of a wider question which had increasingly troubled FAO and, indeed, other U.N. organizations, during the 1950's. Most of the underdeveloped countries were overwhelmingly agricultural and were receiving increasing aid. But what assurance was there that all of this was not scattered, hit-and-miss help? Without a national development plan and without people competent to make a plan and execute it, how could anybody know whether the country was making the best use of its own resources and of the aid it asked for and received? In the absence of logically determined priorities, was anything permanent being built?

FAO had no specific planning mandate and neither did anybody else. However, through its concern with forestry and soil fertility and because of special conditions in the countries bordering on the Mediterranean, FAO began in the early 1950's to make studies which were destined to grow into a full-scale planning approach to national and regional development. Mediterranean countries continue to receive major FAO planning attention, but the approach has potentialities for other countries and regions, notably in Africa as we shall see in the next chapter.

There is nothing more basic in any agricultural country than soil and water, and in the Mediterranean countries these are intimately related either to forests, or lack of them. The similarity of conditions which prevail in areas bordering the Mediterranean, whether they be in the southern regions of France, Italy, and Spain, or in Syria, Lebanon, or in the northern regions of Tunis and Morocco, has long been noted. In these and other Mediterranean areas, severe poverty and ignorance exist. All have roughly similar climates and all suffer from deforestation, soil depletion and erosion.

The striking contrast between the position once held by the Mediterranean world and its present economic and social condition has long been a matter of international discussion and concern. Since World War II study missions from many national and U.N. organizations, including the Economic Commission for Europe and the World Bank, have visited every country bordering the Mediterranean to explore what could be done to break the vicious circle of poverty and lagging development. A number of national and regional development programs have been initiated, notably those in Italy's Mezzogiorno, France's Bas-Rhone and Languedoc regions, and in Spain.

In FAO, raising the fertility of the Mediterranean region has always been regarded as a major objective. So impressed were the founders of FAO by the damage of progressive deforestation and soil depletion in arid countries of the Middle East that they added forestry to the basic program of the new Organization. One of FAO's first missions was sent to Greece in 1947 and its recommendations became basic to that country's planning. After that, FAO's concern for the Mediterranean led to the establishment of various technical commissions and working parties to study the problems of the area. The FAO Regional Forestry Commission for Europe and that for the Near East combined to sponsor a joint Mediterranean Forestry Subcommission to formulate a forest policy in the entire Mediterranean region. In time it became apparent to all concerned that forestry could and should play a new role in the rehabilitation of Mediterranean countries, for erosion, unused hilly or mountainous lands, and wasted water were of the essence of poverty there.

In 1957 FAO, with the assistance of world-renowned economists and specialists from the U.N.'s Economic Commission for Europe, launched the ambitious "Mediterranean Project". Initially centered on forestry, it was subsequently widened to include all land and water resources. The object was not only to survey resources but to draw up development programs covering forestry, pastures, water, and related agricultural improvement. Not only would technical solutions be offered, but investment costs would be appraised and complementary measures in the fields of social, economic and fiscal policy, and public information and education would be recommended. Agricultural and forestry development were to be considered in relation to the nation's wider resources and within the context of a national plan. One of Dr. Sen's first major recommendations to the FAO Conference in November 1957 was for the conduct of Mediterranean studies along these lines.

FAO completed and published in 1959 its survey entitled "FAO Mediterranean Development Project — The Integrated Development of Mediterranean Agriculture and Forestry in Relation to the Economic Growth — A Study and Proposals for Action". This was accompanied by ten* elaborate country development studies made by expert teams working closely with officials and specialists of the countries themselves. Morocco was one of these countries.

One of the chief conclusions reached in these studies has become of major significance. It was a recommendation for concentrating resources and attention within each country on "spearhead development zones". That is to say, it was recommended that scarce technical knowledge, financial resources and human competence should not be scattered over the entire country but concentrated on a few favorable zones. The theory was that if the income, taxable

---

* Morocco, Tunisia, Lebanon, Syria, Iraq, Spain, Yugoslavia, Greece, Israel and Turkey. Other country studies were subsequently undertaken.

capacity and investment resources of these favorable zones were increased, their effects could be spread outward to neighboring regions. In this way, progress could become more rapidly self-propelling and self-sustaining.

Since 1959, FAO has helped the Mediterranean countries concentrate their efforts on spearhead zones. However, progress would have been extremely slow if the U.N. Special Fund had not come into existence in 1959. The spearhead zone idea seemed made to order for the pre-investment purposes of the Special Fund. Thus, upon the foundation of the Mediterranean Project studies, FAO and the Special Fund have moved along in fruitful collaboration.

The new government of independent Morocco, confronting its ocean of problems, was enthusiastic about the Mediterranean Project from the first and cooperated fully. Moreover, it was the first to apply to the Special Fund, in December 1959, for help in financing a spearhead project to be executed by FAO. Its choice lay in the poverty-stricken Western Rif mountains. This is by no means a favorable zone. In fact it is one of the least favorable. Nevertheless, there were compelling reasons for approving it.

The most favorable zone, as already indicated, lies in the Sebou Basin immediately to the south of the Rif. But clearly it was useless to try to improve the Sebou Basin unless the flood waters, the silt, the poverty-stricken unemployed, and the political discontent of the Western Rif were somehow restrained from inundating the cities, valleys and plains below. As if to emphasize the point, nature unleashed in 1960 the most disastrous floods of recent times in northern Morocco, engulfing half a million acres of the best land in the Sebou Basin with from 1 to 3 feet of Rif mud.

Project DERRO (Développement Economique de la Région du Rif Occidentale — Economic Development of the Western Rif Region) began operations in April 1961, financed to the extent of $702,800 by the U.N. Special Fund and $1,180,000 by the Government of Morocco. FAO is the executing agent, and it works closely with Morocco's OMNR (Office Nationale de Modernisation Rurale), a new, lively organization established by the King of Morocco, which has been given extraordinary powers and funds. OMNR has

Work Centers scattered in the rural communes of the Rif and the Sebou Basin, equipped with agricultural and forestry machinery and some know-how but far too few trained men. Before the spearhead zone projects got under way, OMNR was scattering its effort with little effect, but it soon added purpose and method to its enthusiasm. After two and a half years, Special Fund financing of DERRO project ended in May 1964, but OMNR is carrying forward the work under plans made and according to methods demonstrated.

The headquarters of DERRO are in the handsome buildings of what used to be the French Air Force School in Fez, now being converted into the University Mohammed V. It is a busy place. The ten FAO experts of six nationalities, plus a Moroccan staff of thirty, seemed twice the number as they sat over their drafting tables or bustled about carrying huge volumes. There are maps and charts all over the place. Directing this operation for FAO is an ebullient, vigorous Dutchman, G. Veldman, for whom the time it takes to finish a sentence is too long, and for whom a 15-hour work day is totally inadequate.

DERRO's assignment was to prepare for the Western Rif a plan of action for the next five years and more general plans for 10 to 20 years; to make detailed plans, with budgets, for the development of seven chosen "zones of attack", each comprising from 45,000 to 70,000 acres. It was also expected to draw up even more detailed blueprints and carry forward actual work in a pilot zone of 2000 to 4000 acres in each of the seven "zones of attack". This was an ambitious undertaking, and partly as a consequence of administrative changes and confusion in Rabat, all of it has not been accomplished in the time allotted. But a great deal of it has, and the work is continuing.

The studies and blueprints that have been produced would weigh a ton. Highly technical, they include, among other things, airphoto maps, soil maps, soil fertility maps, present and proposed land use maps, data on the numbers of families, their scatteration, education, income, outlook, and information on land ownership and tenure. Detailed execution plans include specifications as to how small individual properties are to be joined to make possible common banquettes that drain without erosion; which cereals and which fruits should be grown where and in what combination; which fertilizers should be used; which areas should be reforested and which reserved for free grazing; which kinds of cattle and which sheep and goats should be kept, where and how should they be fed in all seasons. And, of course, they include detailed budgets. This merely gives a beginning of an idea of the complexity of agricultural planning in a backward area.

Perhaps the most important achievements of DERRO have yet to be mentioned. Those are the training of OMNR personnel all the way from the field staff back to headquarters in Rabat, the lessons learned in working with the village chiefs, family chiefs, and the individual farmers, and what the farmers themselves have learned from the demonstrations in the pilot zones.

In the company of Mr. Veldman and Mr. Tsouli, the young Moroccan director of OMNR's nearby Work Center in charge of local operations, I visited the Oued Mellah pilot zone near Taounate, 50 miles north of Fez. Stretched before me was a natural bowl of great beauty containing about 3000 acres which, except for the walls and terraces which had been built, would have descended rather too sharply to the bottom. In this bowl, the owners of small plots had been persuaded, and also paid (with cash and with food supplied by the World Food Program), to join their properties and build contour earth banquettes which hold moisture and, being inclined, allow surplus water to drain off harmlessly at the end. There were fields green with new crops. There were newly planted fruit and olive trees nearly everywhere one looked. There were steep hillsides covered with new pine striplings. Nearby was a new agricultural experiment station where seeds and new crops are tested before being recommended to the local owners. There also the local farmers are taught modern farming and forestry methods, including the breeding and feeding of improved livestock. Two hundred beautiful white-and-pink Swiss and Spanish milk goats, recent arrivals, were sheltered there looking as out of place as would have been Folies Bergère chorus girls. Their care and feeding and breeding, and their eventual distribution to private owners, is an important part of the enterprise. An FAO expert imported from Switzerland was there to teach milk use and conservation and cheese-making.

Before we left Oued Mellah the local village chief appeared, beaming, proud of all he surveyed, and without waiting for introductions, shook hands with all present. It was a good sign.

One cannot be too certain what will happen to Project DERRO as the FAO experts depart. In fact, it is important that some of them remain, and that the United Nations keep a careful eye on the situation. The main trouble is in Rabat where, with unbelievable capriciousness, the limited number of competent administrators are obliged to play a continuous game of musical chairs. Hardly has a department or bureau or office head begun to learn his job than he is shifted to another and entirely unrelated post. No matter how much outside help is received, a country cannot improve its condition and make permanent use of projects such as DERRO unless there is firm direction and continuity in capital headquarters.

Hardly had DERRO got under way than FAO, the Government of Morocco and the Special Fund began considering another spearhead zone in the more promising Sebou Basin. It was logical. The Western Rif can never, even in the most optimistic view, be made prosperous. The most that DERRO can do in the Rif is to bring about sufficient human and physical improvement to keep the "Rifains" on their farms and prevent Rif poverty and discontent and mud from swamping the rest of the country.

Prospects for the Sebou Basin are different. There, through building dams for water impoundment and flood control, through extending irrigation, introducing new crops (such as cotton and the sugar beet), educating the farmers in more modern curing methods, and attracting new industries to transform agricultural products, a large area can be made prosperous. In fact, the Sebou can be made wealthy enough to support improvement of the Rif without strain. The studies required in the Sebou project are fewer and less ponderous. Attention there is focused more on drawing up specific investment proposals which will attract capital.

"Project Sebou", in effect the child of DERRO, began operations in late 1963 with headquarters in Khenitra, where the Sebou River flows into the ocean. The U.N. Special Fund is furnishing $1,246,000 and the Government of Morocco, $3,203,000 for 3 years. FAO, in charge of the project, supplies the manager, Mr. G. Oved of France, all the technical specialists, and needed equipment. Morocco's National Irrigation Office (ONI) is the counterpart. When I visited Khenitra in February 1964, seventeen international experts were already at work on the scene, aided by about fifty Moroccans. ONI was full of enthusiasm, and great things are expected.

Morocco has on paper a national development plan, but it is scarcely worthy of the name. In any case it is not followed, which may be just as well. But the Government aspires to an effective national plan. That is why it has welcomed DERRO and SEBOU — for they bring a method of planning and adapt it to Moroccan needs and then train local officials to carry out the plan. That is also why the Government invited the World Bank to make an economic survey in the spring of 1964. And that is also why FAO, the U.N. Special Fund, and the Government of Morocco have agreed to undertake a third planning project covering the development of all the country not already under the scrutiny of DERRO and SEBOU. The new enterprise is PRAM — Project for the Modernization of Agriculture in Morocco. In seven zones outside the limits of possible irrigation, PRAM will make an inventory of physical and human resources, work out detailed plans for using them to best advantage, and as in the Rif, pay special attention to a smaller zone of attack. And in each zone, it will develop fully a pilot demonstration area of 2000 to 3000 acres. Fewer and less elaborate studies than in the Rif are expected, but more training of the farmers and of the professionals in OMNR who must direct and supervise operations.

The Special Fund is contributing $1,157,600 to the 5-year PRAM enterprise, the Government of Morocco $4,800,000. Operations began in May 1964. FAO is in charge of the work and its Moroccan collaborator is the OMNR, mentioned above, which has already gained experience in DERRO. The three FAO/Special Fund projects, plus the World Bank survey, should enable the Government to elaborate an effective national plan, train people to carry it out, and expose the farmers to new ideas and methods. The Government of Morocco, more than most governments, is thoroughly convinced that its modernization must begin with agriculture.

Morocco is only one of ten Mediterranean countries in which spearhead zones are already subject to FAO pre-investment planning with U.N. Special Fund support. In three others — France, Italy, and Spain — spearhead zones are being tackled by governments without outside aid. The ten zones vary considerably in physical characteristics and potentialities, but are nevertheless bound by many common problems, and the principles worked out in the Mediterranean project can be applied to all.

The Antalya region in Turkey has complex problems of land and water use. Deforestation and erosion underwrite poverty even though there is a potential for irrigated agriculture and manufacturing. How best to overcome these problems is being studied in one FAO/Special Fund Project. But already, as a result of preliminary findings, government investment in irrigation, agriculture and transportation in the area have doubled.

In Greece, the Western Peleponnesus is poor because of low productivity, and because it is unproductive it has become to a considerable extent depopulated. Both agriculture and industry need reconversion to new crops and products which may find outlets in the Common Market. The Government of Greece as an initial step has already greatly improved its extension and other services in the region.

In Tunisia and Egypt, semi-arid zones near the Mediterranean require the stabilization of nomadic populations, range management, water conservation, and the introduction of new cereal and tree crops.

In Syria, the problem involved in the spearhead zone is resettlement of poor farmers in an area where vast reserves of ground water (discovered in the course of a previous U.N. Special Fund survey) makes possible irrigation. In the Lebanon spearhead zone the improvement of a mountain economy and its integration with that of the plains is the problem, and in Jordan the emphasis is on forestry. Iraq and Cyprus have still other problems.

In all of these projects the focus is on agricultural improvement as the regulator of overall economic development. All involve planned land use and the techniques of planned land and water development. All inevitably impart training in planning methods, all seek to strengthen training institutions, and all try to bring about a modernization and extension of government services to agriculture and forestry. Moreover, all are intended to lay the basis for public and private investment. Incidentally, the preliminary recommendations of the planning teams are useful in suggesting ways in which the Freedom from Hunger Campaign and the World Food Program can contribute to the larger enterprise.

In concentrating here upon method and individual country efforts, we have temporarily lost sight of the wider aim of the Mediterranean project, namely to restore at least a part of that prosperity which during most of man's recorded history the Mediterranean countries enjoyed. But that vision is not absent from the thoughts of those who carry forward the Mediterranean work. In fact, now that many country initiatives are under way, the regional aim and conception are coming more to the fore.

As far as geography, climate, and agricultural potential are concerned, the Mediterranean countries stand in relation to Europe where Florida and California stand in relation to the United States. They are warm, they are vacation lands, they are producers of winter vegetables and semi-tropical fruits when the rest of Europe is frigid and its inhabitants are eating a dull winter diet. With proper development and organization, there is no reason why they should not become as prosperous in relation to Europe as are the two American states in relation to the U.S.A. It is significant, however, that it was only as they became prosperous from agriculture and tourism that the American states attracted industry on a large scale.

There are nevertheless high hurdles in those qualifying words "with proper development and organization". We have already taken a look at the obstacles to development. But even as those may be cleared, organizational problems which have their roots in national sovereignty and separateness become more apparent. If, for example, the consequences of increased production and marketing of fruits and winter vegetables are not to be glut and unremunerative prices, there should be some advance regional planning of production along rational lines. And obviously, all the countries would profit, even now but more so in the future, from common marketing arrangements and machinery. The idea of a Mediterranean "Cold Chain" — a regionwide system of refrigerated storage and rapid transport to European markets — is ever present. Studies have been made, and although no action has yet been taken to build the "Cold Chain", it is definitely in the cards for some future time.

Mediterranean development is not going to require just planning and pre-investment, but investment — a great deal of it. The question of a Mediterranean Development Bank has been studied and discussed, but for the time being, at least, has been shelved. The World Bank and other development-financing institutions are regarded as being, for the present, sufficient, especially in view of the new alliance between FAO and the World Bank which was described in Chapter 6 of Part II. A host of other questions — export promotion, market development, trade barriers, advertising, and many others — are coming along and are being studied.

There have been two major intergovernmental meetings of the Mediterranean countries, one at Bajadoz, Spain, in 1961, and one at Nîmes, France, in May 1964. These were primarily concerned with exchanging views and experiences, and with refining methods. The relation of the work being done in spearhead zones to national plans has been one of the principal subjects of study. However, the Nîmes Conference went further than ever before in considering national development in relation to that of the Mediterranean as a whole. It recommended going ahead with the creation of three Marketing Institutes to be linked through a central organization located in Rome. This step was encouraged by an advance statement from the Special Fund that it would consider sympathetically applications from groups of countries for Special Fund support for the creation of marketing institutes.

Apart from what the Mediterranean Project may have done for the countries of that region, it has had profound effects upon FAO as an institution. One might suppose, as I had done, that FAO had always studied regional and country problems, gained some conception of priorities, and then focused all the knowledge and expertise of its technical and economic dimensions upon those problems in a rational way. But not so! This procedure, logical as it is, more or less began with the Mediterranean Project. Before that, FAO responded to the requests of governments without being able to steer them in the direction where they should, with most profit, go. Moreover, government requests went to FAO's technical and economic divisions which responded with high degrees of independence.

The Mediterranean Project brought about new working methods in FAO: assistance to the Mediterranean countries is now "integrated". Work in each spearhead development zone is supervised by a headquarters Steering Committee composed of representatives of all relevant technical and economic divisions who together focus the knowledge of their technical specialities upon the problems involved in the zone. Moreover, these Steering Committees report to and are supervised by a high level Mediterranean Advisory Committee, an intra-FAO organ which has pioneered the transformation of FAO into an integrated development agency.

In the original Mediterranean Project survey, credit was given to three FAO men then occupying modest positions in the Organization. One was Egon Glesinger, a forester of world reputation, who has been with FAO since its inception. For many years Deputy Director of the Forestry Division, he became Director of Forestry in 1959, and in 1963 was named an Assistant Director General. But for 4 years he has been, and he remains, the dynamic Chairman of the Mediterranean Advisory Committee. A second was Henry Ergas, who drafted the 1959 survey. He was in May 1964 made Director of the new FAO/World Bank Cooperative Program. Since 1960 a very active member of the Mediterranean Advisory Committee, he is now in position to continue, even more effectively, his role in Mediterranean development. The third person to whom credit is due is A. C. Janssen of FAO's Economic Analysis Division.

The regional approach to development has been so successful that countries in many areas far from the Mediterranean have asked for similar treatment. As we shall see in the next chapter, FAO in 1961 undertook an Africa Survey. The facts gathered in that survey, and more importantly, the principles and methods which were suggested by it, are helpful guides to action as nearly three dozen independent countries of that continent start on the long road toward modernization.

CHAPTER 2

AFRICA

IT is impossible for our generation to appreciate fully the main events of its time. Gigantic and dramatic, highly disturbing, obscured by detail, they are beyond the capacity of the mind and the emotions to register. How can one appreciate, and face day after day, the implications of atomic fission, the world population explosion, the shattering of empires, and the emergence of sixty new and independent states? It is impossible. Therefore, we accept them as casually as a soccer match riot in a neighboring state, put them out of mind, and occupy ourselves with more limited and comfortable matters. If histories are written two centuries hence, the awesome happenings of our generation can be depicted in bold outline and comprehended. For most of us who live through them, they exist only occasionally and remotely.

A hundred years or so ago the continent of Africa, except for coastal fringes, was unexplored and unknown to the civilized world. By the turn of the century it was divided up, at least on the map, by European colonial powers. Twenty years ago there were only three independent countries in the entire continent: Ethiopia, Liberia, and South Africa. Today, there are about three dozen and more on the way. It is of course absurd to count states by the dozen, and that is why I have chosen to do it: it is impossible to grasp the reality of thirty-six independent African nations, of whom twenty-six have become sovereign only in the last seven years. Three years ago I visited sixteen of these countries in 30 days. It was a numbing experience to be   exposed, however superficially, to the problems of so many countries in such a short time. My instinct was not to write a book about Africa but to forget about it.

Since then, I have visited three other African countries at more leisure. Observed singly, they take on reality and one becomes engaged with their friendly people, with their hopes, and with their problems. And then, one has only to multiply by thirty-six! Each of the countries of Africa is trying not only to maintain its independence and internal order but also to build as fast as possible a modern society. It seeks to bridge a gap of centuries in learning, in health, and in the acquisition and application of modern science and technology, so that its people may be well-fed, well-clothed, and have the opportunities enjoyed in the more advanced countries of the world.

Even if the United Nations had sought to do so, it could not have avoided heavy responsibilities for helping the new countries of Africa as they assumed the burdens of independence. Over 80 per cent of the people in those countries are directly dependent upon agriculture or fishing or forestry, conducted with primitive methods. Literacy is less than 20 per cent, debilitating diseases are rampant, and hunger and malnutrition endemic. Government administrative and technical services are depleted by the departure of the European officials and technicians. Largely innocent of industry, the countries exhibit in extreme form all of the characteristics of underdevelopment. Not only is there vast unemployment and underemployment of people, but also of land. With population increasing at a rate of 2 to 2.5 per cent each year and with soil fertility declining, the situation grows more critical. Most of the countries, upon achieving independence, promptly applied for membership of the United Nations and its agencies. The U.N. family braced itself for a flood of requests for help, which were not slow in coming.

FAO's knowledge about actual conditions in the African countries and the technical problems with which it would have to deal was inadequate. National plans for agricultural development, if they existed at all, were rudimentary. It was clear that if the countries were to make the best use of their resources and outside aid, agricultural improvement should be planned in the context of economic development as a whole. In order to respond intelligently to calls for help or embark upon long-term programs of assistance, FAO needed far more information and a clearer idea of priorities.

The Mediterranean Project had shown a way of proceeding and had already proved its worth. The Director General therefore proposed an African Survey to the FAO Council in October 1960 and was authorized to proceed forthwith. Thus, with the cooperation of the U.N. Economic Commission for Africa, the International Labor Office, and UNESCO, FAO organized international teams of experts who reviewed existing studies, and made first-hand investigations in a number of African countries. In all, thirty-three countries in tropical Africa were covered. Early in 1962, FAO published the Africa Survey and seven detailed individual country reports. The Survey, while making no pretension to completeness, allowed FAO to reach tentative conclusions and establish priorities which are proving to be useful guides to operations.

The root of poverty in Africa lies in the extreme backwardness of the 80 per cent of the population which lives directly from the soil, the forests, and rivers and oceans. This being so, it was concluded in the Survey that "under present African conditions, industrial development depends more on rural progress than rural progress depends upon the development of industry. Limitations on the growth of manufacturing", the Survey continued, "are due in part to the absence of adequate policies for industrial development, but perhaps primiarily to the inadequate growth of the rural sector and the consequent small size of the market. . . ." An increase in the ability of farm people to buy even simple manufactured products "is impossible without an increase in their productivity". Primary emphasis should therefore be on rural improvement. While investments are clearly needed in industry and in roads, transport, and communications, these should in the early years be planned to help relieve the backwardness of agriculture. For example, investments in small-scale industries involving the processing of local agricultural, forestry, and fishery products were favored.

Improvement in nutrition was found to be "of paramount importance" to economic and social progress. Governments should aim at an increase of 10 to 20 per cent in food production for home consumption. This could be accomplished partly by reducing losses in storage and transport. Special attention should be given to protein foods: meat, milk, poultry, eggs, fish and fish meal, and processed oilseeds. Modern systems of canning, dehydration, and freezing of food should be investigated. Research in food technology should be undertaken, preferably on a regional basis.

Primary emphasis being upon improvement in rural standards of living, the Survey recommended that governments stress community development, cooperatives, rural credit, and adaptation of antiquated systems of tribal land tenure to more modern economic conditions. Above all, it urged education and training for rural progress.

The greatest hope for progress in Africa resides in training the young. Education should therefore be planned so as to make the school the center of rural development with the teacher assuming a key role in each community. The importance of teaching and agricultural service must be fully recognized, and the elementary school act as the center of rural renascence.

These and many other significant conclusions emerged from the Africa Survey. Groups of countries were urged to build research institutions and plan their trade and industry together in order to make better use of resources and secure the advantages of wider markets. Initial concentration of development efforts in "spearhead zones", as in the Mediterranean, was recommended. And the importance of improving government services was spotlighted.

Tropical Africa is receiving considerable aid from individual countries, notably France, the United States and Great Britain. It is also receiving substantial help from the European Economic Community and many of the U.N. agencies, notably UNESCO, UNICEF, WHO, and FAO. Nevertheless, all outside aid is not expected to rise above 5 per cent of African national incomes. The main burden of progress must be borne by the countries themselves. If they are to achieve a 5 per cent growth in *per capita* income each year, they must invest each year not less than 20 per cent of their national income — an extremely difficult thing to do in very poor countries. If they succeed, if foreign aid increases reasonably, and if the countries overhaul their economic and social structure as suggested by the FAO Survey, they may be able to double *per capita* income within 15 years. That average yearly income is now roughly estimated at $75 per person and includes the incomes of the rich in the cities. In 15 years, if all goes perfectly, $150 average income per person! This is the reality.

In line with the chief recommendation of the Africa Survey, FAO inaugurated in 1962 a Special Program of Education and Training in Africa, which continues today. General education advisers financed by the United Nations are helping the African countries determine their agricultural education needs, draw up plans for meeting them, and find whatever outside money is required to do the job. Specialists in such subjects as cooperatives, fisheries, food technology, veterinary medicine, are serving as consultants to African governments and institutions as they plan the improvement of their agricultural education programs or start new ones. Short-term training centers and seminars organized by FAO are helping improve the administration of ministries of agriculture. And meetings of senior agriculture educators and administrators in Africa have been helpful.

All of these things are being done under the Special Program in Africa. At the same time FAO in collaboration with EPTA, the Special Fund, and UNICEF, has also stepped up its usual kinds of operations in tropical Africa. All of this seems small in relation to tropical Africa's needs and aspirations. But in Africa, as elsewhere, there are limits to how fast progress can be made, even with all the help in the world.

Faster progress may be made in a few of the more advanced countries such as Nigeria. In 1963, FAO sent a large survey mission to that country to make a detailed assessment of its potentialities, establish guidelines for agricultural progress and help revise national plans. This study made, FAO and the World Bank are now jointly looking into investment opportunities which were discovered.

Dakar, the capital of Senegal, is without question one of the most attractive cities in Africa. Located on an elevated headland jutting out to sea, largely surrounded by water, its French-built portion is relaxedly modern, replete with splendid avenues and scenic coastal drives, and generously furnished with trees and flowering shrubs. The native portion itself has wide streets, openness, and relatively little of the visible squalor found in so many African cities. But the most picturesque features of Dakar are its tall and beautiful women decked out in colorful creations known as "boubous". The boubou is contrived of perhaps 10 yards or so of handsome material of several matched colors; it drapes and flows gracefully, and it is worn off one shoulder. Also, it is accompanied by a head scarf tied and worn with style. A Senegalese lady in her Sunday boubou strolling down the avenue reminds one of nothing so much as a stately galleon of fantasy under full, multi-colored sail. It is nevertheless somewhat disturbing to be interrupted at a Monday morning U.N. office meeting by the entrance of a secretary so dressed.

In stark contrast to Dakar is the countryside round about. Covered with untidy and undistinguished scrub, dry and brown in February, its monotony is relieved only by the beobab tree. Seen solitary on a landscape, as often it is, the beobab tree has a certain grotesque beauty and it is revered by the Senegalese. Its huge, porous, trunk produces absurdly small branches which in turn produce absurdly small leaves, and its wood has little commercial use. Life is poor and hard for those who live in the land of the beobab tree.

If one focuses exclusively upon the statistics of African poverty, he is discouraged. If he concentrates upon the amenities of Dakar, he is beguiled. And if he dwells upon the symbolism of the beobab tree he loses all hope. Fortunately, in Senegal there are alternatives. One can consider the aspirations and activities of vigorous and enthusiastic young men whom President Senghor has gathered about him to run the government, and their plans to improve conditions. Also, one can study the remarkable efforts being made by other countries and by U.N. agencies to help them carry out their plans.

I propose to describe briefly here what one U.N. expert has done during the last 3 years. He is making what may some day be regarded as a profound contribution to progress in Senegal. And he is helping the Government of Senegal to pioneer a pattern of action which may be of great significance to at least eight countries of West Africa.

Chosen by the Nutrition Division of FAO, paid for by the U.N.'s EPTA, and invited by the Government of Senegal, Jean

G

Mocquard, food technologist, citizen of France, went to Senegal in April 1961, a year after the country's independence, to advise the government on how to expand its food industry. At first glance it might seem odd that a new country needing almost every kind of help should, as a matter of priority, seek a food technologist. Also, it is difficult to see how the work of a food technologist in Senegal could be other than of peripheral significance. However, a special set of circumstances made the need for his services acute and his work of key importance.

The economy of Senegal is overwhelmingly dominated by a single crop, peanuts, and closely tied to the economy of France. Eighty per cent of the country's exports consist of peanuts and peanut products, almost all sold to France. However, Senegalese peanuts are not competitive in the world market, but have been heavily subsidized by the French Government under annual quota and price agreements. Now that Senegal is independent and France has joined the Common Market, the subsidies are ending. Finding ways to diversify agricultural production is not a matter of choice but of survival.

The chief dish of the Senegalese, rich and poor alike, is couscous. It has a cereal base and is eaten with a sauce of peanut oil and whatever condiments, fish, meat and tomato paste, the larder can provide. In Senegal the couscous base is millet, a vulgar grain for which there is no commercial market. It is eaten mostly by the people who grow it. The preparation of a single meal of millet requires many hours of backbreaking work by the woman of the family. Thirty miles from Dakar, alongside the paved highway, I saw two women, old before their time, pounding ears of millet in a hollowed stone as it must have been done 3000 years ago. They were removing the grains from the cobs. After that, with mortar and pestle, they had to make a flour, and then cook the flour — hours of work for a single meal. The creation of a commercial market for millet and the building of industries for preparing millet flour are, then, clearly desirable.

Millet may not seem to bear a very close relation to peanuts but, as we shall see, it does. The government of Senegal in 1961 established an Agricultural Marketing Office (L'Office de Commercialisation Agricole) known as OCA, to exercise a monopoly over the marketing of the great cash crop, peanuts, grown on half of Senegal's cultivated land. The individual growers were induced by a variety of incentives (reasonable credit, free transport for crops, and better prices) to organize cooperatives. The OCA, buying from the cooperatives, and already having a marketing control, thus acquired a monopoly over the purchase of the peanut crop. The Senegalese peasant, receiving higher prices, honest treatment, and many side benefits, is far better off than he has ever been before, and President Senghor has called OCA "the keystone of the Senegalese edifice". As the peasants have acquired more cash, however, they have tended to spend it on rice, tomato paste, and other imported foods. And it is highly doubtful that peanut sales abroad will be able in the future to pay for such imports. Senegal must therefore diversify its agriculture and produce at home substitutes for the imported products.

As we proceed with this story it is necessary to take account of still another major Senegalese problem and another reason for crop diversification: malnutrition due to protein deficiency. Cattle, signs of wealth, are not eaten so much in Senegal as kept for prestige purposes in many parts of the country, regardless of their quality or yield. There is little fresh meat sold. There is no dairy industry. And although the ocean off Senegal teems with commercial fish, they are not eaten very far inland. The local fishing fleet, consisting of native rowing pirogues, a few of which now have outboard motors, land their catch on open beaches where it is handled under the most unsanitary conditions. I was present one afternoon as the pirogues came in, after a long day's work, to land their catches on the long, broad beach at Kayar, 25 miles northeast of Dakar. At least a thousand people were congregated on a half mile of sand, watching, cleaning fish, filleting them, buying, selling. It was a colorful sight, but I did not want fish for dinner.

Without refrigeration or organized marketing there is little question of fresh fish reaching beyond the coastal fringe. Some fish, locally dried in the sun, reaches inland and the Senegalese like it. But it is prepared and handled under unsanitary conditions and in the hot weather it easily spoils. There is not much of it, and it is expensive. Five modest fish factories in Senegal can tuna and some sardines, but mostly for export.

With little meat or fish or dairy products, a large proportion of the Senegalese people living inland do not get enough proteins to keep them well and vigorous. Not only is there protein deficiency but a great deal of actual hunger in Senegal during the months immediately preceding the November peanut harvest. Producing nothing but peanuts, selling them for cash, and spending the cash, the peasant and his family are often hungry during "l'hivernage" — the 4 months June to September.

With these threads identified, we can now examine how they were woven by a U.N. expert.

Jean Mocquard's first task was to study Senegal's food problem in its wider context and make a report, with recommendations, to the government of Senegal. Meanwhile, he got to know the key men in the government and in local business circles. Discussing problems with them, working with them, a plan of action began to emerge. Mocquard leads by ideas, suggestions, and presenting facts. But there is no one in Dakar with whom he has been associated professionally who has not given him full credit for what has happened.

The first step officially decided upon, as early as October 1961, was the creation of a Government Institute of Food Technology to foster food industries in Senegal. This did not come into legal existence until February 1963, but meanwhile Mocquard, working with whatever and whomever he could find, moved ahead fast. When the Institute actually started operating, a great deal had already been accomplished.

The Director of the new Institute of Food Technology is an engaging, energetic young Senegalese by the name of Papa Diouf, graduate in biology of the University of Paris. He and Mocquard occupy adjoining offices. To help Diouf prepare himself for his new assignment, Mocquard arranged an FAO fellowship which allowed Diouf to attend a training institute on canning in France during 1962. Then at Mocquard's suggestion the local U.S. Aid Mission arranged the financing of a several months' trip by Diouf to visit food factories and technical institutes in the United States. These eye-opening trips gave him knowledge, confidence, and prestige, and he returned on fire with the potentialities of his job. Four Senegalese engineers who finished their studies in France and took their degrees in July 1964 have likewise, as a result of Mocquard's arrangements, been sent to Europe and the United States for specialized study with FAO and U.S. assistance. Returning, they will join the Institute.

The Institute operates through four services which are, as yet, skeletons. One conducts studies and enlists the participation of private capital and industry. A second supervises pilot plant operations. A third conducts laboratory experiments and applies the necessary inspection and controls. And a fourth promotes the sale and consumption of new food products. To help the Institute in its early stage, Mocquard secured through FAO the assistance of two other French workers. One of them is N. Y. Claret, who carries on promotion and commercialization. The other is J. C. Trorîal who, provided by the French Freedom from Hunger Campaign Committee, is in effective charge of the laboratory.

By far the most far-reaching undertaking of the Institute, one which, if successful, will affect the economy and perhaps the health of the entire country, is the production of a new flour, called "Farine 21" (because it contains 21 per cent protein), made from 75 per cent of millet and 25 per cent of peanut flour. What is left of peanuts after the oil is extracted is rich in proteins and, properly processed, can be mixed with millet to make a flour suitable as the cereal foundation of couscous. It has been made in a pilot plant and preliminary calculations indicate that it is cheaper than pure millet flour and acceptable to consumers. It is also to be marketed in pre-cooked form, an "instant couscous" which can be prepared in 5 minutes instead of all day.

But if millet is not a commercial product in Senegal, how can the new flour be made? How can the peasants be induced to buy it and how can they afford it? There are answers. The Government's Agricultural Marketing Office (OCA — described above), which has acquired such successful monopoly over the purchase of peanuts through cooperatives, is undertaking to create a commercial market for millet. Through price, transport, credit, and other incentives, the cooperatives will collect the millet from the peasant farmers and sell it to OCA. The OCA will sell it to mills producing protein-enriched couscous. The new flour will then be sold to the peasant farmers through the cooperatives. The results are expected to be a domestic outlet for a substantial proportion of the peanut crop previously exported, a country-wide improvement in nutrition and health and tremendous labor-saving on the farms.

Essential to the success of this and other government efforts to build the national economy and improve nutrition is the participation of private capital. The record thus far is good and prospects even better.

Converting each year 250,000 tons of peanuts into oil and cake for export, Lesieur Afrique S.A., a private French-owned company, is the largest processor of peanuts in Senegal. Lesieur has joined with the Institute of Food Technology and the Senegalese Development Bank to create a new company known as SEDAC (Société du Developpement de l'Arachide et de Céréale) which is perfecting the production of Farine 21 in a pilot plant and will undertake large-scale commercial production. Lesieur is contributing the majority of the capital, the Development Bank the minority. By charter, the Institute of Food Technology is represented on the Board of Directors. M. Patrick Pinon, Director of Lesieur in Senegal, is also Director General of SEDAC.

Impressive hills of peanuts covering acres, a confusing assemblage of machinery, conduits, and tanks, provide the backdrop to the modern air-conditioned offices of Lesieur Afrique in Dakar. There, M. Patrick Pinon spoke confidently about the prospects of his association with the government in the new enterprise. This was the pattern of Senegalese development, he said, and his company was happy to cooperate in making it a success. Moreover, he expected it to be profitable.

The Farine 21 pilot plant was not working when I visited Lesieur Afrique. There was a good reason: the plant had no millet to work on. Because there has never been a commercial market for millet, there was no stock to buy. Happily, the U.N./FAO World Food

Program had agreed to furnish 7000 metric tons for pilot plant operations, and the supplies were on the way.

A number of other food companies have been organized, all following the SEDAC combination of majority private capital, minority public capital (Senegalese Development Bank) and the participation of the Institute. One of these, the SDAI (Société de Developpement Agricole et Industriel), is undertaking, with the help of farmers' cooperatives, to grow tomatoes on a pilot plot of 70 acres in a climatically favored area, and plans to construct there a pilot plant for making tomato paste. The object is to build a local industry capable of supplying Senegal's requirements, which are now imported. Another company, SOSEPA (Société Sénégalaise de Produits Alimentaires), is producing canned meats in sauce, suitable for couscous. A few varieties have already been produced in a pilot operation, and under the trade name of DIAMBAR are undergoing consumer tests. Two other private-public companies have been formed to exploit more effectively the tuna, found in quantity in the ocean off Senegal's shores.

Meanwhile, the Institute has produced in its own laboratory and pilot plants a number of other comestibles, for which it is carrying on consumer tests and hunting for investors. One is a smoked, protein-rich fish flour, hygienically packed in plastic bags, and another is dried slabs of fish similarly packed. These and all other products developed by the Institute bear the trade name DIAMBAR.

Also labelled DIAMBAR is the most important product of the Institute thus far: an enriched baby food containing ingredients which can prevent the dreaded kwashiorkor. With the help of a FAO/EPTA specialist, five mobile vans supplied by the French National Committee of the Freedom from Hunger Campaign, and a national press and radio campaign, this baby food is now the subject of wide promotion. It will also be used in school feeding programs. Incidentally, those who are popularizing DIAMBAR baby food are also promoting the other protein-rich foods of the Institute.

More plans are afoot than can be recorded here, but a final one must be mentioned. About 80 miles south of Dakar, situated on a long sandy spit at the mouth of the Saloum River and not far from Bathurst and the mouth of the Gambia River, is the community of Djifère, in the heart of one of the richest and most varied fishing grounds on the entire coast of Africa. Shrimps, oysters, sardines, anchovies, mackerel, squid, and larger deep-sea fish abound in the area. Substantial fishing is conducted in pirogues and by antique methods, and dried fish is prepared there for sale inland.

But Djifère also has an industrial plant which has up to now treated local titanium sands. With the exhaustion of the raw material the company is closing down operations and transferring its activities elsewhere, leaving an industrial complex, complete with buildings, wharf, power plant, hospital, school and cooperative. Several hundreds of people will be left unemployed. Mocquard has worked out plans for transforming the complex into a modern sea food processing industry capable of supplying Senegal and many other African countries, as well as Europe and the United States, with a great variety of frozen, canned and smoked products. The project has not yet jelled and may not do so, for if Senegal and Gambia agree upon an economic union, nearby Bathurst, capital of Gambia, may be favored as the site of the new industry.

The President of Senegal, Léopold S. Senghor, is one of the outstanding men of Africa. Cultivated, highly educated, he is guided as he seeks to build his country by a political philosophy which is compounded of deep religious faith, socialism, and practicality. The pattern of the incipient but hopeful food industry of Senegal reflects his philosophy: a combination of private capital, government finance, and public power to achieve economic and social ends. Those ends, moreover, are not purely nationalistic. Not only the President but most of those in positions of influence in his Government are imbued with the idea that whatever development patterns Senegal evolves, whatever industries are created, whatever educational and research institutions are created, must not only serve Senegal but, also as far as possible, neighboring states. The pattern evolving in Senegal is believed to be applicable to at least eight West African countries, and the Institute and the individual food industries being planned and built have conscious regional aims. Six government officials in different departments affirmed this to me with impressive emotion and conviction. "And if we fail, all West Africa fails." This may not be, strictly speaking, accurate. But it reflects a splendid spirit.

The Senegal Institute of Food Technology has proceeded from the beginning on the hope, and even the assumption, that it would receive help from the U.N. Special Fund. But it did not sit and wait for help. It went far and fast with organization and plans. Thus, when the Special Fund in June 1964 approved aid to the Institute in the form of much-needed experts, equipment, and training for future Senegalese staff abroad, it was almost an anticlimax. The Special Fund is contributing $690,000 to the Institute's work over a period of five years, and FAO is the executing agent. However, FAO and EPTA had already been "executing" for 3 years.

CHAPTER 3

THE UNITED NATIONS AND THE ALLIANCE FOR PROGRESS

THE Alliance for Progress is generally regarded as an American affair, the allies being the United States of America and twenty countries of Latin America. It was so conceived by President Kennedy, it is so considered by the U.S. Congress which votes appropriations for the Alliance, and it would never occur to most well-informed citizens of the United States to think otherwise. As for the Latin Americans, the Alliance means money, technical help, and pressure from the United States. It is seldom suggested in public print that the United Nations and its family of organizations have anything to do with the Alliance for Progress. And because very little that the United Nations family is doing to promote progress in *any* part of the world reaches the public in North America or Europe, the impression is prevalent that progress in the countries south of the Rio Grande depends exclusively upon the efforts of the Latin Americans themselves aided by the United States.

The Alliance aims, of course, at economic and social progress generally, but it spotlights specific objectives. They include planned use of resources, land reform, tax reform, education, better health, nutrition and housing, social welfare, more efficient agriculture, increased local and foreign investment in productive enterprise, and rising standards of living. And as instruments for improving the lot of rural people the Alliance favors not only land reform but also cooperatives, rural credit institutions, agricultural extension services, and agricultural training schools. But these have been aims and emphases of the United Nations and its family of organizations in their Latin American activities for about 15 years!

President Kennedy's call for an Alliance for Progress and the United States promise to help finance it over a period of 10 years were acts of statesmanship. They furnished enormous inspiration, pressure, and means for speeding up the pace of development in Latin America. And the Charter of Punta del Este, signed on 17 August 1961, refined the goals of progress and introduced organization and method, with special emphasis upon national development planning. However, when anyone starts working in Latin America in an Alliance program and gets down to the level where actual work for progress is being done, he finds that the United Nations has been there for some time and is still there, working hard at his elbow. Without detracting in any way from the splendour of the U.S. initiative, generosity, and Alliance effort in Latin America, it can be said unequivocally that the United Nations and the members of the U.N. family of organizations, strongly supported by the United States, are close and effective allies of the Allies for Progress.

There might not be an Alliance for Progress today — certainly not one with such emphasis on land and tax reform, education, national development planning and *social* progress — if the U.N. family had not been hard at work there for more than a decade. Washington had not shown much interest in Latin American affairs during the 1950's until the Cuban revolution showed its color. The words "social development" did not enter the American aid vocabulary until 1960, aid to education had scarcely been thought of in Washington, and if anyone had proposed suggesting to Latin Americans the need for land and tax reform he would have been promptly vetoed on grounds that such things are just not said in relations between sovereign states.

How was it, then, that when President Eisenhower and the State Department began to speak of these things in 1960 they were met with such informed and enthusiastic response from governments in Latin America? The Act of Bogotà, signed by the American States on 16 September, covered the waterfront on social progress in no uncertain terms, almost as thoroughly as the Charter of Punta del Este a year later. The leaders at Bogota and Punta del Este were the Latin Americans themselves. How could this have come about?

Unease inspired by the Cuban revolution was working on the

Latin Americans, but there was more to it than that. Nearly every idea of the Alliance for Progress had been studied, discussed, and promoted for years in the United Nations Economic Commission for Latin America (ECLA) and had been furthered by the U.N. agencies, notably FAO, UNESCO, UNICEF, ILO and the World Bank. For a long time FAO had played a leadership role in agrarian reform, urging, advising, studying, helping wherever it had a chance to do so. ECLA (the U.N. Economic Commission for Latin America) had taken over the idea and the emphasis from FAO and, in addition, had promoted development planning, tax reform, and redistribution of income as essential to progress. Its economic and social studies in these and many other fields had set the tone for progressive thinking. The Inter-American Development Bank was based upon ideas and initiatives of ECLA. Without any question, ECLA, under the direction of Raoul Prebisch, its Executive Secretary, had a profound philosophical impact on Latin America during the 1950's.

The father of the Economic Commission for Latin America (ECLA) is considered to be Dr. Hernàn Santa Cruz of Chile. While Chairman of the United Nations Economic and Social Council (ECOSOC) in 1948, Dr. Santa Cruz led the fight to establish the Latin American branch. Santa Cruz has for 5 years now been FAO Regional Representative in Latin America. A member of one of Chile's leading families, a lawyer, an influential liberal known and respected throughout Latin America, Santa Cruz, regardless of position, has always played an important role in the ECLA which he helped to create. However, in his job as FAO Regional Representative, close relations with ECLA are not a matter of choice, but of necessity, for the Latin American Regional Economist for FAO is also in charge of agriculture at ECLA, being Director there of a joint FAO/ECLA agriculture division. It was thus easy for ECLA to build upon FAO's pioneering in land reform, and equally simple for FAO to profit from ECLA's pioneering in agricultural development planning and to become heavily involved in that activity, because the same people had been involved in both. In agriculture, it has frequently been hard to distinguish ECLA from FAO.

Even if, without years of prior cultivation by the U.N. family, the basic ideas of the Alliance for Progress had been acceptable to Latin American governments in 1961, the Alliance would have been slower in getting off the ground had it not been for the hard, patient work of the U.N. agencies over a long period. Their very purpose had been to transfer technical knowledge and capital, open eyes, train people, advise on policies, help build research and training institutions, and help strengthen government services. These are the essence of Alliance aims. Obviously, the U.N. family had not been able to do more than make a start, no more than build a few foundations in men, ideas, policies, and institutions; otherwise, the Alliance would have been unnecessary. But those foundations are of enormous importance.

The work of the U.N. family in Latin America should not, however, be thought of in the past tense, as if it ended when the Alliance started. On the contrary, all U.N. agencies have stepped up their activities in Latin America since 1961. They are laboring hard and effectively, and they are an essential part of any alliance for progress in Latin America.

Strange as it may seem in view of the years of pioneering by the U.N. family, the first draft of the Alliance's Charter considered at Punta del Este did not even mention a role for the U.N. agencies. It was FAO's Santa Cruz who led what became a lively and prolonged struggle for U.N. recognition in the Charter. It ended in the inclusion of a paragraph reading as follows:

> In order to provide technical assistance for the formulation of development programs, as may be requested by participating nations, the Organization of American States, the Economic Commission for Latin America, and the Inter-American Development Bank will continue and strengthen their agreements for coordination in this field in order to have available a group of programming experts whose service can be used to facilitate the implementation of this Charter. The participating countries will also seek an intensification of technical assistance from the specialized agencies of the United Nations for the same purpose.

The Punta del Este Conference not only recognized the United Nations in this manner but also appointed a number of task forces to help governments do the things they had agreed to do in the Charter. The U.N. agencies were invited to join a number of them.

One of the most important of the task forces was the Inter-American Committee for Agricultural Development (CIDA) which is playing a key role in the Alliance for Progress, and FAO is playing the leading role in CIDA.*

CIDA started by assessing all existing information in Latin America useful to agricultural planning, and then launched into a major investigation of land tenure problems and how they affect agricultural development in Argentina, Brazil, Chile, Colombia, Ecuador, Guatemala, and Peru. Teams went to each of those countries, made investigations, and wrote reports and recommendations. Similar studies are in progress in other countries. Also planned is a detailed CIDA examination of Latin American institutions which provide agricultural education, extension and research. Deficiencies will be spotlighted, and recommendations made for remedying them. This study was proposed by FAO and FAO will lead the work. A third project, this one proposed by ECLA, is making a similar assessment of Latin America's needs for fertilizers, pesticides, agricultural machinery and other requisites of modern agriculture, and its capacity to meet these needs. Factors affecting the production and consumption of these are being isolated, and recommendations made to governments for meeting needs. A fourth undertaking of a similar nature relating to agricultural credit has also been launched.

CIDA also sends teams to individual countries to help them plan agricultural development and carry out specific programs. For example, for more than a year and a half a CIDA team, headed by an FAO man, has been helping the Government of Colombia prepare a program of agricultural diversification in the Caldas region, an area which has hitherto grown only coffee. A number of projects recommended by CIDA are already underway, financed by the Inter-American Bank. CIDA work in Colombia has been so successful that the Inter-American Bank has asked FAO to extend the

* CIDA is a committee of organizations: FAO, ECLA, OAS (Organization of American States), and IIAS (Inter-American Institute of Agricultural Sciences — a U.S.-subsidized training and research organization with headquarters in Costa Rica). The Inter-American Development Bank (IDB) has more recently joined CIDA.

assignment of the FAO chief of the CIDA mission for a further year, and the Government of Colombia has asked for CIDA help in other parts of the country.

Another CIDA team under the direction of an FAO specialist is in Brazil. This team is helping the Government create an adequate agricultural planning organization, and also prepare a program of agricultural diversification and improvement in the poverty-stricken northeast province and in Sao Paulo. In Peru a CIDA team consisting of eleven experts, seven of whom are FAO men, is helping the Government to formulate the agricultural part of its economic development plan. Similar CIDA help has been requested by Venezuela, Costa Rica and Bolivia, and missions are either already on the spot or are being organized.

The work of the organizations combining their effort in CIDA has inspired such confidence, and the services of CIDA are in such increasing demand by Latin American governments, that it is now recognized by the United States as the authority on agrarian reform and agricultural development in Latin America. When the Directors of CIDA met in Washington in March 1964, Mr. Teodoro Moscoso, the chief of Alliance for Progress affairs in the U.S. Agency for International Development, appeared before them to express this view and to ask CIDA to extend its land reform work. He said that the U.S. Government had learned, through experience, that it was not in the best position to give advice and technical assistance to the Latin American countries on land reform and that this could best be done by international organizations. The U.S. Government, Mr. Moscoso continued, had followed CIDA's activities with great interest and had come to the conclusion that CIDA was the best instrument for carrying on land reform activities. Consequently, he announced, the Agency for International Development will support CIDA in any programs which it prepares to promote land reform in Latin America and to help the Latin American governments carry them out.

Notwithstanding the importance of FAO's special work within the structure of the Alliance, its chief contribution to progress in Latin America lies, as it has for years, in its own Latin American program.

When FAO first started field operations in Latin America in 1951 neglect and stagnation prevailed in the forests, fisheries and pastures of most of the countries of the region. It was in those fields that governments most wanted help, and it was there that FAO concentrated special attention. After 10 to 15 years, results are beginning to show, and in the next few years they promise to become spectacular. Moreover, as elsewhere in the world, FAO has helped increase local competence to build and operate cooperatives and credit institutions, improve education, adopt modern statistical methods, and deal with animal and plant diseases, animal and plant breeding, and nutrition. Several thousand FAO experts of dozens of nationalities went to Latin American countries after 1950 to help and advise, and thousands of Latin Americans were enabled to increase their knowledge and ability through FAO-aided local training and by specialized study abroad.

Today in mid-1964, the FAO Regional Office in Santiago and the Sub-regional FAO offices in Mexico City and Rio de Janeiro supervise the work of nearly 500 experts, including those paid directly from FAO's budget and those financed by other members of the U.N. family and the Alliance for Progress. The regional and sub-regional directing officers are in touch with the highest officials of Latin American governments and initiate actions, frequently of great importance. The thirty-seven technical specialists assigned to those offices ride the Latin American circuits nearly half their time and, working with government officials at a somewhat lower level, also spark important actions.

Since 1959 FAO has helped prepare more than fifty Latin American projects for submission to the U.N. Special Fund. Of these, forty-one, of enduring significance to research, training and capital investment, have been approved, with FAO as the executing agency. These involve a total expenditure of $75 million, roughly half supplied by the Fund and half by the governments concerned. In mid-1964 twenty-five of these were in operation and the others are in various stages of organization. At least half were originally conceived and suggested by the FAO regional offices which also helped work out the details.

Many of the Special Fund projects executed by FAO have resulted in the creation of new institutions, such as forestry institutes in Chile, Argentina, and Venezuela; a Latin American Institute of Agricultural Marketing in Colombia; fisheries institutes in Peru, Ecuador and Chile; and an Institute of Higher Agricultural Education in Bolivia. Other Special Fund/FAO projects consist in strengthening and enlarging existing institutions; for example, agricultural training and research in the University del Valle in Colombia; the Faculties of Agriculture and Veterinary Science in the Universities of Quito and Guayaquil, Ecuador; the National Institute of Agriculture in Chapingo, Mexico; the Institute of Agricultural Engineering of the University of Molina, Peru; a Veterinary Institute in Peru; the National Institute of Industrial and Technical Research in Balcarce, Argentina; the Inter-American Institute of Agricultural Sciences with headquarters in Costa Rica; and many others.

Long before the Alliance for Progress, FAO invested years of patient, unspectacular effort promoting land reform — making technical studies, giving encouragement, and prodding to action. The land reform laws and projects in Chile, Bolivia, Colombia, Peru, Ecuador, Uruguay, the countries of Central America, and elsewhere are due in part to the help of FAO. In many of these countries FAO regional officials and specialists have worked actively with the government, not only in the preparation of reform legislation, but in its execution. They continue to do so today.

FAO also trains officials in the principles and techniques of land reform. In 1963, with the help of the Inter-American Bank, FAO organized two Inter-American training courses on agrarian reform, one of which was held in Santiago and the other in Bogotá. FAO provided the lecturers. Also FAO specialists have lectured at international courses on agrarian reform organized by the International Institute of Agricultural Sciences and the Inter-American Bank. And as a result of FAO initiative and help, an Agrarian Reform Institute is now being organized in Chile. This is a Special Fund project with FAO as the executing agent. The Inter-American Bank is providing additional funds which will permit the Chilean institute to serve neighboring countries also. For years FAO has pushed hard, and is still pushing, for the creation of an all Latin America institute of agrarian reform.

In spite of past efforts, however, antiquated systems of land tenure are still a major obstacle to progress in Latin America. The commitments made in the Charter of Punta del Este imply that at least half of the peasants in Latin America should within the next 10 years obtain not only land, but also the benefits of education, agricultural extension, credit and technical knowledge. Without these, the overwhelming majority of the peoples in Latin America, living on the land, will continue on the margin of existence, and a satisfactory rate of economic growth will not be attained.

United Nations' assistance to agricultural planning in Latin America is of basic importance. FAO lends direct agricultural planning assistance to governments, and works closely with the United Nations Economic Commission for Latin America (ECLA) which, long before the Alliance, sent advisory groups to help governments in their planning. In 1961 ECLA joined the Organization of American States and the Inter-American Bank in a tripartite group which provided special planning services to governments, with ECLA and FAO doing the work on agriculture. Subsequently, the U.N. Special Fund and the Inter-American Bank financed a Latin American Institute for Economic and Social Planning with headquarters in Santiago. This Institute, in effect a branch of ECLA, renders extensive advisory and training services.

The United Nations insists that planning for agricultural development must be an inseparable part of planning for overall economic and social growth. For unless agricultural planning goes hand in hand with education and training and with industrial development, it cannot succeed. This, learned through experience over the years, is constantly emphasized. The United Nations also insists that planning should not be exclusively national, but to the fullest extent possible should cover all of the countries in any given region.

The 10-year Alliance for Progress was launched only in the fall of 1961 and yet remarks are already heard that the Alliance is a failure. Most of the people are still poor, illiterate, undernourished, and have no land. The rich still hoard their unused land, keep their money abroad, and evade taxes. There is still hunger and unrest, and communism is still a menace.

But what do the critics expect? That with a declaration of intent and an agreement, a few hundreds of millions of dollars dropped into the Latin American machine will suddenly turn out prosperous, educated, contented people, all safe for democracy? It is absurd to talk so soon of failure or success. The aim of the Alliance is a peaceful political, social and economic revolution. But peaceful revolutions are not made overnight, and bloody ones, though they may change rapidly the power structure, cannot quickly change basic economic and social conditions. It is well to remember that it took fourteen years for FAO's efforts in the two limited fields of forestry and fisheries to begin to show results in the relatively well-off country of Chile.

Great things are going on in Latin America, and change is in the air. Whatever else the Alliance has done, it has generated pressure for land reform and concern for better use of the land. These have become favorite subjects of conversation, not only among those who want land, but also those who have it.

In Rio de Janeiro I spent an evening with a group of young people from land-owning families. And what was their persistent subject of conversation? Land reform! They were all in favor of it. I remember especially one beautiful young lady who, through the death of her parents, had been for a number of years owner of several thousand acres of excellent land in the interior of Brazil which she had never seen. "They should take it," she said. "If I don't use it, they should take it. And they *will* take it. I shall scream and protest, of course, but they will take it, and they *should* take it."

In southern Chile I visited a man who is getting rich from cultivating with modern methods 1500 acres of land inherited by his wife. He works 12 hours a day and reads all the technical literature he can lay his hands on. He trains his workers and pays them well, uses fertilizers and modern machinery. His pastures are enriched, his livestock of excellent quality, and his forests well tended and productive. In effect, his is a model demonstration farm. He carries on a friendly running argument with his friend and neighbor who inherited, as did his father and grandfather before him, 10,000 acres of excellent land, part of which is completely unused and untended, and part worked inefficiently by poor tenant-peasants. Rich, living on money invested abroad, the neighbor was clearly on the defensive. And he may change, for the pressures for change, growing even within his own stratum of society, are growing strong. If he does not change, and soon, he may very well lose his land under Chile's land reform law. No land has yet been expropriated in Chile, but the writing is on the wall. Everywhere in Chile, the chief topic of conversation is land reform and land use. It has become quite the thing for at least one son in a land-owning family to become an agronomist and undertake development of the family's land.

There was a thin young man in Chile who, with burning eyes, talked to me about land reform and effective use of land. About 30 years of age, father of four children, a graduate agronomist, he was in his thinking far beyond the other people in the room. He was concerned about what would happen when land was divided among people who did not know how to cultivate it. In fact, he was so concerned that he had recently undertaken to manage as a unit twelve farms that had just resulted from the division of a larger property. This was to be his career.

The 10-year program envisaged in the Alliance is not too long, and it may take all of that time for dramatic progress to begin to register in the statistics of many Latin American countries. But progress there is. The transfer of knowledge, the training of people, the building of institutions are slow processes, but they are sure. The inspiration and pressures of the Alliance are speeding up the process of change. They can be hastened even more with full recognition of the family of the United Nations as allies for progress in Latin America.

CHAPTER 4

NEW FRONTIERS: FORESTRY AND FISHERIES

FOOD and trees throughout history have been rivals for land. To settlers the forest has been an enemy to be conquered, enslaved, and used as a source of firewood, construction timber, and new land for cultivation. It was seldom regarded as a friend by the settler who, trying to grow food, looked upon its continuous threat to cleared land as a standing affront. To primitive, semi-nomadic tribes the forest has been neither friend nor foe but a habitat and convenience, to be used until exhausted. The most explicit enemies of the forest, however, have been men not in search of food or shelter, but of riches. To them the forest has been merely a collection of objects to be cut down and sold. This enmity, carelessness, and greed have caused some of the earth's ugliest scars, created some of today's most difficult problem areas, and brought about some of the world's most extreme poverty.

To most of the people who have ever lived from the earth's soil, the oceans and their products have scarcely existed except perhaps in fancy or fable. Knowledge of the oceans and benefit from their perishable produce has been largely confined to the seacoasts and the cities. This is true even today in the underdeveloped continents of Asia, Africa, and Latin America. In northern latitudes people have always lived from the oceans, and in more temperate climates men with greater knowledge and technology have for centuries gathered food far and wide from the seas. But most of the people who live in half of the world have never been able to depend upon food from the oceans as a significant part of their diets.

Rivers and lakes are of course more ubiquitous and friendly, and in primitive fashion have always been used as sources of food, but their limited produce has seldom traveled very far.

Today we, of necessity, look at forests, oceans, rivers, and lakes in a different perspective. [Hundreds of millions of people who have never had enough to eat are clamoring for more life-and-health-giving food. Exploding populations are pressing harder and harder on the land for food. Dozens of new nations, and dozens more newly awakened nations, are trying to put new knowledge to work to develop their resources and make possible a better life for their peoples, and the more advanced countries are trying to help them. Moreover, modern technology makes it conceivable for these efforts to succeed, and because of new communications and transport the people are aware, even though vaguely, that they can succeed.] But the wisest and best educated ones among them know that this will depend upon the planned, coordinated, more effective cultivation of *all* their resources: not only people and land and minerals, but also the forests and the oceans and the inland waters.

In this new context food and trees, ancient rivals for the land, have become partners in supplying man's expanding needs, and the indifferent and capricious oceans, lakes, and rivers are seen as dependable allies of the land in supplying man's food.

Forestry was originally included in FAO's mandate for a negative reason: because *misuse* of the forests, which occupy one-fourth of the world's land surface, has such profound effects upon agricultural productivity. Forestry is today a highly important and growing sector of FAO's work for reasons which are emphatically positive: because forestry, working hand-in-hand with forest industries, can make such a powerful contribution to development in the countries of Asia, Africa, and Latin America, and because it has been learned that people can grow enough food or earn money to buy food only in the context of overall economic and social development. In the short space of 20 years knowledge and necessity have so grown, along with population, as to change drastically the role of the forest in man's service.

A generation ago conservation was directed almost entirely toward protection of the forests against reckless destruction. Today, conservation is becoming allied to the dynamic conception that forests can be developed to better serve the needs of people and still give due respect to conservation. This alliance is based upon a growing mutual understanding among foresters, forest industries and governments. Foresters, who once could not see people for the trees, are learning that forests must and can be made to serve people's needs more fully without destruction of tree-capital. Forest industries, which once cut and ran, are learning to respect the biological facts of forestry and the limitations upon their freedom of action. And governments are learning to appreciate the potentials of their forests for national development if they impose and enforce conditions to safeguard the forests and provide incentives to forest industries.

It has been an eye-opener to me, as I have traveled in the three underdeveloped continents, to observe the degree to which one or more of the aspects of forestry is involved in national development planning and activity. Without exception, all lands bordering on the Mediterranean and all the countries of the Middle East suffer from millennia of forest destruction. There, denuded land has yielded to erosion and floods, disappearance of topsoil, and aridity. The consequence is poverty, hunger, disease, and ignorance in a never-ending cycle. Charting the road back from poverty, governments are obliged to seek first of all the restoration of the soil and its fertility, and what a job that is! Trees must be planted to serve as windbreaks and as moisture-holders, to help halt erosion and to prevent floods. In many countries this work must be combined with building terraces and banquettes on hillsides, and with dams and reservoirs and irrigation works and reforestation to prevent their silting. FAO is heavily involved in this work.

In Africa south of the Sahara forestry problems and potentials are varied and near the heart of national planning. On the one hand there are magnificent forest resources begging to be put to man's use, and on the other hand there are semi-arid and deteriorating uplands reminiscent of the Middle East. In some areas semi-nomadic tribes destroy the forest, scratch the earth for a few years until fertility is exhausted, and then abandon ruined and eroding land and repeat the process elsewhere. In others, reckless operations are destroying hardwood forests as logs are cut and dragged out for export. And in still others, dense forests remain untouched because of lack of roads and transport. Logging operations are widespread, but forest industries are few.

Most of the countries of Africa south of the Sahara have been independent for only a few years. FAO is active in their development planning councils and much is expected of its advice and help there in the future. For tropical Africa has enormous forest wealth and the natural conditions for rapidly producing more. Proper exploitation of the forests and conversion of the wood by local forest industries could become key factors in national progress.

Most of India is wood-poor in extreme, so lacking in trees that farmers and villagers burn cow dung as cooking fuel instead of returning it to the soil. Extensive efforts are being made, with FAO help, to encourage village fuelwood plantations. These may be the key to a rise in agricultural productivity.

Parts of Southeast Asia are fabulously forest-rich but poor in forest industries, exporting chiefly logs and rough-sawn timber. Reckless cutting has endangered accessible hardwood stands, notably the teak of Thailand, Burma and the Philippines, while inaccessible forests are stagnant. Spurred and helped by FAO, the countries of the area are beginning to take the steps necessary to protect their forest resources, to encourage forest industries, and to put to work their forest capital (while carefully safeguarding it) in the interest of national economic development.

Perhaps the greatest successes of FAO's vigorous doctrine of forest development with conservation have been scored in Latin America. Almost every country in that region is well endowed with forests and with natural conditions for rapid and plentiful renewal. And yet, until FAO came on the scene about 15 years ago, the forests were largely ignored as an important source of national wealth. It takes time for planted attitudes to grow into national policies and legislation. It takes more time for forestry institutions to grow and produce trained foresters and forest services. And this framework is necessary before forest industries can be established which will operate within the boundaries of national policy. But there was a relatively early reception of the FAO forest doctrine in several Latin American countries. Today fifteen years of effort is beginning to pay off in Chile and Mexico in terms of industrial production, import savings, and exports. Brazil and a number of other Latin American countries are not too far behind.

The encouragement of new forest industries in three continents is obviously based upon the assumption of expanding markets for wood products. But is this a valid assumption? As everyone knows, fuelwood is replaced by coal and oil everywhere as soon as people can afford it, and in cities one has the impression that metals, concrete, and synthetics are being used increasingly instead of construction timber. Is not, then, the future of forest products a dismal one?

Quite the contrary. Use of industrial wood products has soared in recent decades and today is greater than ever before. Estimates of future demand are high. Industrial wood products include sawnwood and panels (plywood, veneer, fiberboard, particle board, etc.) used for house construction, for boxing and crating, and for manufacturing. They also include newsprint, printing and writing paper, industrial paper and paper board, and packaging materials. These products are essential to economic and social development in any country, and their consumption in developing countries with low-income levels tends to rise faster than *per capita* income or food consumption. As income rises, families with low incomes spend their first added money on food, but there is a limit to how much they can eat, and their purchases soon level off. There is no early limit, however, to their expenditures for materials for housing, reading and writing, and packaging. In all countries there is a precise correlation between national income per head and consumption of paper and paperboard.

At the beginning of this century paper was produced chiefly from rags in small factories, and world consumption was small. Then large factories began to manufacture paper from wood, and in 1910 the world produced 10 million tons. In 1930, when the world depression broke out, paper production was somewhere between 25 and 30 million tons, and producers were even more depressed than their markets, convinced that their existing capacity to produce had far outgrown even prospective demand. They were wrong. Today the world is producing 75 million tons of paper and paperboard and by 1975 expects to produce 150 million tons. These figures put paper in the same weight class with steel and wheat, and far ahead of all fibers combined.

Advancing wood technology has created new and improved products and vast new markets for them; it has lowered production costs; and it has made possible the use of certain tree species and wood wastes and residues which were formerly ignored or discarded. Today, virtually all varieties of trees and wood residues in the world are usable in products which are in great demand, and there are few underdeveloped countries that do not possess the forest resources to make most grades of paper, paperboard and particle board, and a number of other wood products mentioned below.

Thirty-five years ago both mechanical and chemical processes for making woodpulp favored almost exclusively the dominant coniferous species of the north temperate zone — spruce, fir, hemlock, and pine. Today, mechanical processes can use poplar and aspen as well. New chemical or chemical-plus-mechanical processes for making pulp can use practically any kind of tree or other fibrous raw material, including cereal straw and sugar cane waste. In our generation, wood and wood-based panel production — plywood, fiberboard, particle board, etc. — has grown from a modest beginning to a varied glamor industry of spectacular growth. Fiberboard and particle board (the latter being a postwar product which has already achieved fabulous success) can be made of almost any kind of tree or other fibrous material and is especially adapted to using mill residue, including bark and sawdust. More than any other products, they make full use of tropical rain forests which, containing mixtures of tree species and tangled roots and vines, have hitherto resisted any commercial use.

Advancing wood technology, industry enterprise, and world demand have endowed the forests of the southern half of the world with a potential value undreamed only a few years ago. Most of the world's underdeveloped countries are in its southern half, most of them are forest-rich, and most of them have climate, rainfall, and population-land ratios favorable to rapid forest growth. With forethought, investment, research, and training, exploitation of these forest resources could play an important role in propelling many of the poorer countries of the world along the development road.

Ninety per cent of the world's paper is today produced and consumed in industrialized, high-income countries, that is to say, in Europe, the U.S.S.R., North America, Australia, New Zealand and Japan. And nearly all the world's wood and wood-based panels are produced and used there. But even poor underdeveloped countries use paper, and today, although the raw material stands in their backyards, they are spending about $500 million in precious foreign exchange on pulp and paper imports alone. If, as is expected, their incomes rise over the years, they will be using nearly $3 billion worth of paper and paperboard by 1975. If they should build up their own paper industries they could, by 1975, not only supply their own increasing needs, except for specialties, but earn $1 billion annually from exports, and increasing amounts thereafter.

A number of industrialized countries which are large producers and consumers of wood products, for example Japan and certain European countries, are running into raw material shortages. They are going to have to depend increasingly upon imports either of raw materials or of processed wood products, or both. Production and trade in wood and wood products, however, are highly competitive, and the question is, "Where are these imports going to come from, and in what form?" Will they come from other industrialized countries which still have surplus reserves and production capacity? Or from the developing countries? Will increased imports from the developing countries be in the form of raw material or processed wood products? Unfortunately, it seems likely that countries in southern latitudes will share in the growing market only slowly, and even then with unprocessed or semi-processed raw material, unless they are given more help with their forests and forest industries. Likewise, without more help they are not apt to be able to supply their growing domestic needs for paper. The kinds of help needed are indicated below, but first let us state succinctly the case for help.

We start with the premise that everybody in the world has an interest in the progress of the people of underdeveloped countries out of poverty and ignorance, and that this progress depends primarily upon their using more efficiently their own resources.

As we have seen, most underdeveloped countries are well endowed with forest resources. These are as important a source of wealth as mineral deposits. If properly exploited, they could provide the basis for a beginning of industrialization. It is a generally accepted principle that priority should be given to industries processing raw materials.

Wood industries located in or near the forests have many advantages. Logs are heavy, bulky, and costly to transport. As they are processed, they lose weight and the processed products are easier and cheaper to transport. Work in or near the forests helps relieve rural unemployment, increases incomes where they are most needed, tends to diminish the flow of the poverty-stricken, unemployed to the cities, and trains people for industrial work — all highly beneficial.

Forest industries, as a group, are flexible in their requirements for capital, labor, skills, and raw materials. There is nearly always a wood industry of some kind or size to fit a local situation. In logging, expensive mechanization is frequently not a pressing necessity and can be postponed. Instead, manual labor can often be used to advantage. Wood is relatively easy to work mechanically, and it is possible for small units, with modest capital investment, to be economical in the manufacture of sawn timber, veneer, and mechanical pulp.

Forest exploitation commonly yields wood of different kinds and grades, and the establishment of one kind of operation can lead easily to another that is complementary. Thus, logging can lead to sawmilling and mechanical and chemical pulp making. Sawmilling can in turn lead to the manufacture of plywood and fiberboard, and mechanical pulp making can in turn lead to paper making. And all, with their residue, can encourage the manufacture of particle board. An original initiative tends, therefore, to multiply itself and at the same time induce investment in still other unrelated industries.

Decentralized, backwoods industries create a demand for, and help pay for, roads and power plants which are needed to open up hinterlands. Logging roads may help extend a regional road system, and a hydro-electric plant may encourage the building of a news-print mill which becomes the major customer of the electric plant.

Forest industries are second to none as import-savers and potential export earners for developing countries. Inevitably these countries desperately need imports of manufactured goods and capital equip-ment. But they can import only as much as they can pay for with their exports (plus whatever marginal foreign aid and investment they may be receiving). In the early stages they have only primary commodities or raw materials to export. But the more labor and skill they can add to their raw materials, the more foreign exchange they receive for their exports and the more goods they can import as a result. The addition of labor to forest resources through forest industries is one of the easiest ways conceivable for developing countries to increase the value of their exports, and an even easier way to save the money they would otherwise have to spend on imported paper and other wood products.

Industry and agriculture growing side by side in a country, each stimulating and buying more from the other, and with agriculture, becoming more productive with fewer workers, supplying industry's labor force — this is the picture of a satisfactorily developing country. Forestry is closely related to forest industries. Forest industries can be a vigorous stimulant to agriculture and both a stimulant and valuable addition to a country's economy.

The case for forestry and forest industries as important keys to development did not grow out of the market-place and the keys will not be turned fully and effectively by market forces acting alone. Foresters, forest industrialists, and scientists working in their laboratories in the advanced countries have found a technological basis for "the case", but it has been the world's forest and develop-ment economists, stimulated and aggressively led by FAO, who have made the case for the transfer of forestry knowledge and capital to underdeveloped countries. And it is governments and technical organizations, again with FAO in the lead, who are laboring to create the conditions for the transfer and bring about the transfer itself.

The conditions include first of all greater knowledge which can be gained through research. Technological advances made thus far are the results of research to solve problems which confront the forest industries of advanced countries. But, to quote an FAO study, "the volume of research directed toward solution of the specific problems of the less advanced countries is still negligible". Only incidentally has research revealed the possibilities for establishing successful forest industries in the poorer countries.

To attract and assure the success of forest industries, the government of each country must be convinced of the importance of its forest resources, adopt a national policy, and, seeking whatever help it may need from the United Nations or individual countries, establish schools for training foresters and build up their forestry services. They must — again with whatever outside help may be needed — acquire full and detailed information about their forest resources. Technical experts, studying that information, must then reach conclusions about the potentials of exploitation, and isolate and solve through further research the technical problems. Projects must then be studied within the context of the country's society and economy, with careful attention to transport, labor force, the prospects of capital investment, internal and foreign markets, foreign exchange, and so forth. Useful, indeed necessary for full success, is an overall national development plan embracing a forest development plan.

With these conditions established or on the way to establishment, it will not be too difficult to attract private and public capital for investment in forest industries. But these conditions will be created very slowly unless governments appreciate the significance of the forest resources in the southern half of the world and contribute far more than at present to creating the conditions for constructive use. They can also contribute by trade policies, perhaps in lieu of aid, which will help new forest industries in the southern hemisphere gain a growing share in world markets.

"Go west, young man", was the advice given by Horace Greeley in the nineteenth century to American youth seeking opportunity in the relatively crowded and competitive northeastern part of the United States. Today Horace Greeley, surveying the yearnings for opportunity of the people of the southern half of the world, might well say to them, "Look to your forests", for their forests are a clearly marked frontier, and there lies opportunity.

The oceans and seas which cover more than 70 per cent of the earth's surface are "acre for acre, about as productive as arable land. . . . One to three tons of dried organic matter . . . could be obtained annually from an acre of sea water."* This organic matter consists of animal life (fish, molluscs, and crustaceans), seaweed, and zooplankton. "The aim in fisheries must be toward husbandry, so that stocks of fish can be herded and grazed as a farmer herds cattle."

To those who worry occasionally how earth's burgeoning population is going to be fed, these statements may be comforting, if not beguiling. But let us descend in easy stages toward today's reality.

We can for some time to come set aside seaweed and zooplankton as significant contributors to the food supply, until growing pressures of population on land and animal resources in oceans and rivers make them more competitive. This leaves us, for immediate practical purposes, with fish and shellfood, and here prospects are somewhat more encouraging. Seafood contributes only 1 per cent of man's total food and 10 per cent of his animal protein, but its supply has more than doubled in the last 10 years (it was 41 million metric tons, live weight, in 1961), and FAO conservatively estimates that production in *known* fishing areas can be doubled again without damage to resources. Most commercial fishing is still confined to the continental shelves which make up only 10 per cent of the world's marine area. With more knowledge and exploitation of presently uncharted fishing grounds, production could undoubtedly extend far beyond that — but nobody knows how far.

Commercial fishing has been revolutionized in the last 15 years. Increasing numbers of modern fishing ships equipped with electronic devices for locating fish and using new kinds of fishing equipment

* D. C. Finn, *Fish, the Great Potential Food Supply*, FAO, Rome, 1960, p. 1.

now roam over thousands of miles seeking fish in ocean areas not previously exploited. Many of them are floating canneries as well. On shore, large-scale commercial enterprises have mushroomed, and modern processing and marketing organizations have changed drastically the patterns of domestic and international trade. Government and industrial research has been greatly expanded to meet the requirements of long-range oceanic investigation and to pave the way for adaptation of engineering and food technology to fish production and trade.

As might be expected the industrialized countries in northern Europe, the U.S.S.R., North America, and Japan have led the way in this modernized fishing enterprise. However, sizeable new trawlers and purse-seiners have been introduced at certain points in India, Ceylon, and West Africa, and spectacular recent extension of fisheries in Chile, Peru, and South Africa is based on modern equipment.

A fisherman in a poor country, operating offshore in a primitive rowing boat with traditional gear, is lucky if he catches one ton of fish in a year, while his counterpart in a modern Arctic trawler may catch that much in two days. However, if incentive and demand are present, even simple improvements in small boats and gear, for example installation of outboard or inboard motors and the use of nylon nets, can bring about much larger catches. FAO has been promoting the mechanization of fishing craft and use of more efficient gear in India, Ceylon, Ecuador, Chile, Malaya, Jamaica, Senegal, and a number of other countries, with good results. Catches multiplied five to ten times have been reported from Bombay and Ceylon. Thus, belated adoption of the simpler inventions of industrial society are today increasing fish catches in a number of the poorer countries of the world. However, most of the fishermen in the three underdeveloped continents still fish without benefit of modern times.

About 15 per cent of world fish supplies comes from inland waters, that is to say, from subsistence fishing of wild stock, from commercial fishing in large lakes and river systems, and from fish culture in the fresh-water areas of China, Indian, and Japan and the brackish waters of Taiwan, the Philippines, and Indonesia. A great deal of this production is from the wet rice paddy fields in southeast Asia and Far East. Great potentiality exists for increased fish supply from inland waters, but this requires improvement of waterways, protection of migratory paths, and control of fishing. Fish culture in impounded waters, ranging from domestic ponds to large reservoirs, could also provide larger catches, and the kinds of fish culture practised in the swampy, brackish waters of Indonesia and the Philippines could also be widely adopted elsewhere.

Fish are high in the animal protein which, as pointed out elsewhere in this book, is so deficient in the diets of most of the people living in the southern half of the world that it undermines health and vigor. But with a few exceptions, the countries most in need of protein-rich seafood are far from sharing proportionately in increasing world fish production. Most fish are internationalists, or at least non-nationalists. They live in or have free access to the international waters of the high seas, and are prey to the most efficient fishermen of whatever nationality. In ever-greater numbers, huge fishing boats and floating canneries of well-fed countries are taking fish in the high seas off the shores of countries severely handicapped for lack of protein food. In the port of Dakar I saw large fishing ships from Japan, the United States, and the Soviet Union, laden with frozen fish for home consumption, docked for repairs and supplies. Only a few miles away was an open beach where Senegalese fishermen were landing their pirogues and spreading out small catches to be sold to the first comer or to rot in the sun.

The United Nations' purpose in fisheries development is to help improve nutrition, better the life of rural people, and promote economic growth. Its immediate aim is not to increase fish production generally but to help bring about a larger supply in those countries where the need for animal protein and for economic progress is most urgent. This requires several things, the first of which is action on a broad front by national governments, for the problems involved in creating a fishing industry and a market for fish products are beyond the capacity of private initiative in backward countries. Secondly, it demands outside technical assistance and capital

H

investment. Thirdly, it calls for international cooperation and research to learn more about the oceans' fishing resources and the limits of exploitation without destruction. And eventually it will require scientific international management of fishing resources for the enduring benefit of all countries. Not only could national efforts to measure and exploit marine resources be advanced by international cooperation, but, even more important, they are now being frustrated for want of it.

Mechanization of fishing boats and use of more efficient gear are only the beginnings of a fishing industry. There must be repair shops for motors and modern gear, and fishermen must be taught to use motors and navigate out of sight of the shore. There must be fishermen's docks, unloading machinery, and refrigerated storage for a product extremely perishable in hot climates. There must be refrigerated transport for fresh fish, and factories for drying, canning, preserving, or freezing them. There must be a commercial sales network and credit facilities. There must be continuous research. And, above all, there must be a market. As a rule, people living inland are strangers to fish products and frequently must be persuaded to eat them. This means an extensive education and advertising program. And these varied, specialized activities can be carried on only by local people who must be trained for them in each country.

International action needed for the management, conservation and development of the world's fishing grounds for the common good is too vast, varied, and technical to describe here. Fishing technology and economics have changed so rapidly that their potentials are not widely understood in spite of the dozens of organizations which have sprung up to gain knowledge and use it cooperatively. Most of these organizations are regional; some are worldwide. Some are governmental, some private industrial; some are concerned with science and technology, some with economics and trade. Most of them concentrate on specific fish species, such as tuna and halibut; others, on general fishery statistics, research and conservation. These bodies are extremely useful in helping bring a measure or order out of the chaos of fisheries beset by gales of change on the high seas. But this work is not well coordinated and its benefits are not as widely beneficial as they could be. There are glaring gaps in the total effort: many regions and subjects are neglected entirely. Certainly, not enough effort is being made to systematize and extend fishery knowledge to the countries which need it most.

FAO has the U.N. mandate for gathering, systematizing, and spreading knowledge regarding fisheries, but the rising flood of knowledge and need has swept wildly around it, with the result that there is no world fisheries organization doing an adequate job. The budget and organization of the FAO Fisheries Division were laid out before the current flood, and although they have shared in the growth of the Regular Program budget, the initial structure was too small, and normal budget increases have not made the Division big enough to maintain today's load. This is the one technical field within the FAO mandate where the Director General has failed to press the FAO Conference vigorously for funds. In fact, a unique situation has arisen in which the FAO Conference is pushing the Director General! At the November 1963 session of the Conference, dissatisfaction with the inadequacy of the Fisheries Division boiled over and resulted in a Conference resolution, pushed by rich and poor countries alike, instructing the Director General to come up in 1965 with proposals to insure to FAO the status "of being the leading inter-governmental body in encouraging rational harvesting of fish from the oceans". It also instructed him to insure to FAO's Fisheries Division "full recognition in the Organization and among other interested bodies that concern themselves with . . . fisheries". The requested proposals are being prepared.

There are some services which FAO alone can provide on a world-wide basis and today many of these services are inadequate. FAO fishery statistics are neither comprehensive enough nor deep enough to provide foundation for stock assessment and management in developing fisheries. FAO's economic intelligence and analysis are limited. Likewise, FAO is deficient in training people for fisheries administration, in improving the techniques of fisheries development planning, in studying and helping with national legislation affecting fisheries, and in organizing cooperative fishery exploration. Moreover, there are dozens of fishery fields in which other international bodies are rendering services (limited for the most part to a geographical area, or a fish species, or a function) without planning and coordination of the kind FAO should be doing. These include the assessment of fish abundance, fishery management, food technology, fish utilization, fish harbor development, and many other technical fields.

The FAO Fisheries Division has not had the staff, budget or the status to collaborate effectively with many of these international bodies, much less to provide a world framework for their activities. Meanwhile, international ocean research is becoming increasingly fragmented, with the result that it is losing its focus on exploiting ocean resources to meet human needs. FAO's Advisory Committee on Marine Resources Research has strongly recommended that FAO take immediate steps to devise a world program of marine resources research which would provide a framework for the work of coordinating regional and national research bodies. This would reveal wide gaps, and the Advisory Committee emphasizes that FAO should proceed to fill the gaps.

To highlight the deficiencies is not to say that the United Nations has not done a good job in rendering aid to governments in the development of fisheries. In fact, one of the significant reasons why FAO has fallen behind in the basic and longer-range aspects of its work is that it has been doing so much to help governments with their immediate problems of fishery development. While Regular Program budget for fisheries has lagged, U.N. money for technical assistance in fishing development and for Special Fund fishery surveys, training, and institution-building has become increasingly available. Fifty-five per cent of the staff time of FAO's Fisheries Division is spent on technical assistance and Special Fund projects, and even so the Special Fund is receiving applications for major fishery development projects so fast that the FAO Fisheries Division is finding it difficult to handle them.

United Nations help is in large part responsible for the spectacular growth of fishing industries in Chile and Peru, and has laid the foundations for similar growth elsewhere in Latin America. It has also brought great benefits to India, Ceylon, Indonesia and other countries in southern Asia, and is moving to do so in Africa. But a great deal remains to be done to help underprivileged countries improve their fisheries to meet the nutrition needs of their people while at the same time protecting the world's fishery resources.

The world's waters, like its forests, are a frontier which can be used far more effectively to serve man's expanding needs.

CHAPTER 5

FREEDOM FROM HUNGER

EVEN if the world were so organized as to make possible a massive transfer of food from the richer countries of the world to the poorer, and even if the world were disposed to attempt the transfer, all the world's hungry and undernourished could not even then be properly fed. Moreover, international charity feeding would be no more of a permanent or satisfactory solution than it is among the unemployed of the Appalachian Mountains or of south Chicago. If there is one lesson that has been learned from our generation's concern with world hunger it is that hunger and malnutrition will be abolished only as their victims have the knowledge, education, method, organization, incentives, and means to grow enough or buy enough, and eat enough, of the right kinds of food.

Freedom from hunger has always been a distant goal of the United Nations. But over the years the United Nations' conception of the problem of hunger has broadened, its means have increased, and it has steadily acquired more knowledge of how to work effectively toward its goal. At first it could only, through FAO, supply technical knowledge to governments by means of publications and meetings. Then the U.N. Expanded Program of Technical Assistance made it possible to send technical experts to advise governments personally and directly on how to get specific jobs done. After that, the U.N. Special Fund was created to provide the means to help countries to survey their resources, build enduring training and research institutions, create more effective government services, and prepare the way for capital investment. From there the United Nations moved wisely into helping governments plan their agricultural modernization as a basic part of national plans for economic and social improvement. And there — in balanced economic and social development — it found what it now considers to be the ultimate remedy for hunger and malnutrition.

Underdeveloped countries are overwhelmingly agricultural, without any possibility of becoming sophisticated, industrialized societies overnight, or over a thousand and one nights, or, as far as most of them are concerned, over ten thousand and one nights. Nevertheless, agriculture has had to make its way laboriously in international development councils against the ambitions of poor countries for steel mills and against the ideas of some economists who could not see beyond rapid industrialization as a cure for poverty. It is only in the last few years that agricultural improvement has been fully recognized as basic in the international war on poverty and hunger and that it has taken its proper place in plans for balanced economic and social development. As this has occurred, the Food and Agriculture Organization of the United Nations has found itself more and more out in front, facing the harsh realities of hunger, poverty, and rapid population growth described earlier in this book.

The United Nations works as a family, but FAO is the only member of the family having explicit and primary responsibilities for world agricultural improvement. The United States, Great Britain, France, and a few other advanced countries extend substantial aid to world agriculture, but it is a matter of choice and convenience: they can increase or decrease their aid at will, they can be selective as to recipients, and they can respond or not respond to requests as they wish. But being charged with international responsibility, FAO must always be there. It must respond to the extent that it has the resources to do so. And it must lead.

Out in front, expected to lead — and yet, where and in what condition are the troops? Scattered, and appallingly uninformed either of certain dangers ahead or of the long, sustained, complex campaign needed to prevent disaster. A few people in each country are aware of the situation, a few men in each government know the facts and the probabilities, but they are islands in a sea of unawareness, and the masses of the people are uninformed about the worsening food conditions of the world. If this is true in the advanced countries, it is even more so in the underprivileged countries. There, most of the educated *élite*, having witnessed bottomless misery around them all their lives, are inured to it, accept it as a fact of life, and are little concerned about remedies. And as for the masses there, they may be stirred by expectations of bounty, but it seldom occurs to them that they, as individuals, can do anything to improve their condition.

Food is something that vitally affects every man, woman and child every day of his life. And yet, until four years ago, neither FAO nor any other international organization has assumed any responsibility for speaking to people on this subject, or for encouraging people to speak to people, or for stimulating private interest and initiative in informing people. There was no organization charged with building up public support for private and government action in either rich or poor countries to meet clearly mounting danger. This deficiency, long felt in FAO, became increasingly alarming in the 1950's as the population returns rolled in and were compared with food production trends.

People in most other organizations can read the facts about the population explosion, enjoy a few moments of fright, sigh, and turn to more comfortable subjects. Not so, FAO. For 60 million people added to the world's population each year, most of them in the poorer countries where hunger and malnutrition are already national afflictions, must somehow be fed. This steady, fantastic increase in food consumers necessarily enters into all FAO calculations. If FAO spokesmen at times sound strident, it is because they are aware that existing efforts in most of the countries of Asia, Africa, and Latin America, where populations are growing at 2 to 4 per cent a year, are doing little more than feed the new mouths without making much inroad upon the backlog of poverty, ignorance, hunger, and malnutrition. They know that in many countries and regions food supply is not even keeping up with population growth.

The U.N. agencies are sometimes criticized for not launching a crusade for population control. But they are only creatures of member governments, and most of those governments remain silent on the question of population control. They can and do point to population facts and consequences. But if, without a mandate from their members, they should undertake population control missions in the world they would wreck themselves and accomplish nothing. If governments want international programs for population control, they should speak out in the United Nations and in the agencies. If and when they do, the U.N. agencies, especially FAO, WHO and UNESCO, can then join in to help do something about the problem, but not before.

Meanwhile FAO is in an exposed leadership position in the war on hunger. There are already so many young people in the world, progeny of the postwar population surge — young people who will have families — that even if the birthrate were to decline suddenly and dramatically tomorrow, the United Nations would still have a Herculean job to help the world feed itself as well as it is fed today. But national ambitions are to raise existing standards, to roll back hunger and malnutrition! This will be extremely slow and difficult to do, if it can be done at all, until the population increase is brought within reason. And yet, it must be tried.

Egypt's population is increasing so fast that by the time the Aswan Dam is finished and other schemes to extend cultivated land are completed, the pressures of people on the land will be no less than now. And in Morocco it is figured that if the potentially rich Sebou Basin is fully utilized as planned by 1980, population will have so increased that the *per capita* income in the region will be the same as now. One can scarcely imagine what the situation would be in the world if aid and development works were not in progress now.

The most extraordinary efforts are needed to get through to men and women on the subject of mass hunger. To most educated, healthy, well-fed people living in well-fed countries, nothing is more unattractive than hunger, ignorance, and disease. They are things to be avoided, to be thought of only when necessary. Hunger is something felt before mealtime; ignorance is what schools are for; and disease is something for which one calls a doctor or goes to a hospital. If hungry hordes behead a queen or besiege a presidential palace, or if disease becomes a plague, that is interesting. And people are of course moved to pity by the *sight* of whatever poverty, hunger and misery they see about them, and to civic generosity by the needs of their community. But in the abstract, those hideous spawn of poverty — hunger, ignorance, disease — are to a large degree meaningless. And abstract they are if they affect a billion people living so far away.

The human mind cannot encompass a billion persons, or even a million. If hungry and ignorant people are voters in one's own country who can affect one's own life and destiny, they are significant. But a billion *hungry* people living in distant lands! Pass me the sports page, please.

Many of the same people who make generous contributions through their newspaper when they read of the details of a single starving child, and see its photograph, oppose "foreign aid". If it is difficult for them to respond to poverty and hunger in the abstract, it is equally hard for them to appreciate that two-thirds of the human race, caught up in a tide of rising expectations, confident of better lives, are not going to be, when frustrated, peaceful or pleasant neighbors on this planet.

Not long after he took office as Director General of FAO, Dr. Sen realized that FAO and the United Nations were going to need hundreds of millions of unofficial allies if the world was to be fed. FAO and the other members of the U.N. family receive their support only from governments and act only through governments. And yet, massive hunger and malnutrition in the world is or should be everybody's business. If properly informed and mobilized by governments, Dr. Sen believed that individuals, organizations, and business firms the world over might be induced to take initiatives which could be important additions to what governments and international organizations could do. Thus, he began to put together ideas for what became the worldwide Freedom from Hunger Campaign, inaugurated by FAO on 1 July 1960.

The idea travelled a long road and received many amendments before it became a fact. Dr. Sen first outlined his proposal to the U.N. Economic and Social Council in July 1958. Notwithstanding the increasing efforts of national governments and international organizations, he told the Council, the spectre of famine still continued to haunt the world. One of the reasons, he emphasized, was spectacular population growth resulting from the dramatic success of medicine and public health measures in saving and prolonging lives.

Heroic efforts would be needed if all the people of the world were to be provided with enough food for a healthy and vigorous life. The problem is human want on a broader scale, he said, but hunger provides the focus to all efforts to relieve it, and as the battle against hunger lies at the heart of FAO's work, the proposed campaign was a fulfillment of the task enshrined in FAO's Constitution. However, he added, the problem of hunger was so vast and complex that FAO would need the cooperation of governments, the entire U.N. family of organizations, and non-governmental organizations and foundations, in planning and carrying on a freedom from hunger campaign.

A year later, after the campaign proposal had been thoroughly considered, the U.N. Economic and Social Council endorsed the project and invited all U.N. agencies, governments, and non-governmental organizations to cooperate in it. Meanwhile, it was discussed at the October 1958 Session of the FAO Council, studied and amended by a Committee, and at the FAO Conference in November 1959 the Freedom from Hunger Campaign was authorized. Although it was realized that freedom from hunger was a distant goal, the initial term of the Campaign was fixed at 5 years.

The naming of the Freedom from Hunger Campaign was the subject of debate. Dr. Sen had proposed the name Freedom from Hunger Campaign because it was specific and calculated to evoke emotional response. But there were other suggestions, including one for a World Economic Development Campaign. He won out, but he made it clear from the outset that freedom from hunger could be solved only in the context of freedom from want. Not only must there be enough food available, he said, but people must have enough money to buy food — the most nutritious food they can purchase within their income. FAO's task in helping to free the world from hunger was to advise and assist governments on the use of their agricultural resources for promoting general economic development, for increasing food supplies, and for improving nutrition. But there was need for the active cooperation of all U.N. agencies in dealing with other aspects of the problem of human want, including especially illiteracy and disease.

The Freedom from Hunger Campaign (hereafter referred to as

FFHC) was slow in getting off the ground. The FAO Conference in November 1959 voted only $25,000 for it because the money for organizing FFHC and coordinating its work during 1960 and 1961 was expected to come in the form of voluntary contributions from governments and private sources. Although during those two years about $300,000 was actually contributed, two-thirds of it came in so late in 1961 that it was carried over to 1962, by which time the FAO Conference had provided $850,000 for 1962-3 headquarters costs. National FFHC Committees were also slow in getting organized, so that it was only in 1962 that FFHC really began to make headway. Since then, it has gathered momentum.

FAO plays an important role in stimulating, supplying and co-ordinating the activities of FFHC, but the backbone of the campaign consists of national FFHC committees blessed and for the most part organized by governments. Ideally the national committees should consist of representatives of professional, religious, philanthropic, educational, health, labor and business organizations and also include members of government, of the press and radio, and outstanding private citizens. Most of them, however, fall short of this ideal: many are still purely government committees and others may consist of representatives of a few organizations. By June 1964, FFHC Committees had been organized in 72 countries, but of these, less than 20 could be called active, and most of these were in developed countries. Among the most successful national committees are those in Great Britain, France, Denmark, the Netherlands, Sweden, Ireland, Switzerland, Australia, New Zealand, Canada, Madagascar, India, Ceylon, Malaysia, and Tanganyika. FFHC committees have done less well in the poorer countries than in the richer, for obvious reasons: fewer educated people, lower incomes, poor communications, a dearth of public service organizations, lack of interest and initiative and lack of experience in organizing public information and welfare programs. They need more stimulation and help from FFHC headquarters than headquarters has been able, with its small budget, to provide. Nevertheless several underdeveloped countries have shown that initiative and vigor can overcome many obstacles.

Although few national committees have been doing hard work, the performance of FFHC in its short life has not been unimpressive. It is not meaningful to describe the achievements of the national FFHC committees in monetary terms, for most of the work is done by volunteers without pay, many of the activities require no financial outlay, and educational impact cannot be measured in money. Nevertheless, in less than 3 years the national FFHC committees have raised considerable sums of money and are spending most of it on FFHC projects in underdeveloped countries. The amount known to FAO is $38 million.

The overriding purpose of the Freedom from Hunger Campaign is to inform and educate people in all countries on the problem of world hunger, what needs to be done to solve it and what *they* can do to help. Interpreting education in a broad sense, it also seeks to help people to learn what can be done about the problem of hunger by *doing* something about it. This is ambitious, and the Campaign, addressed to all levels in both rich and poor countries, is complex and variegated: it depends upon the ingenuity of the national committees and the special talents of the people working with them.

At the intellectual level, the foundation of the Campaign consists of 15 basic studies* prepared by FAO and other U.N. agencies. In recent years speeches, newspaper stories, and magazine articles have been filled with impressive facts about food supply, food consumption, malnutrition, and population pressure on food. If anyone should wonder where the figures come from, the answer is

---

* *Basic studies:* (1) Weather and food (WMO); (2) Development through food — a strategy for surplus utilization (FAO); (3) Animal disease and human health (FAO); (4) Marketing — its role in increasing productivity; (5) Nutrition and working efficiency (FAO); (6) Education and training in nutrition (FAO); (7) Population and food supply (U.N.); (8) Aspects of economic development — the background to Freedom from Hunger (U.N.); (9) Increasing food production through education, research and extension (FAO); (10) Possibilities of increasing world food production (FAO); (11) Third World Food Survey (FAO); (12) Malnutrition and disease — a major problem of the human race (WHO); (13) National development efforts (U.N.); (14) Hunger and social policy (ILO); (15) Education and agricultural development.

likely to be one or another of these basic but simply written FFHC studies.

Building upon this foundation of fact, the Freedom from Hunger Campaign extends all the way from an esoteric paper delivered before the Royal Statistical Society of London to the instruction Girl Guides in Ceylon are receiving on how to grow spinach and prepare a well-balanced meal. In between those extremes are thousands of educational and informational initiatives of such variety as to defy summary. Through the press, radio, television, and periodicals, information on hunger and how to combat it is spread. Governments make declarations, prominent men and women deliver speeches and lend their patronage to fund-raising and educational campaigns, seminars and lectures. Special efforts are made to introduce the subject into school curricula. Youth groups, religious organizations, trade unions, international associations are cultivated: they may be persuaded to start educational programs, or join in fund-raising campaigns, or both. Cities, towns, provinces conduct public information drives. Museums put on special exhibits, and FFHC themes are introduced into the dance, painting, music and sculpture. One hundred and forty-six countries and territories have issued beautifully designed Freedom from Hunger stamps. Some of these have been contributed to FFHC, and their sale has netted $200,000 for the Campaign.

The British FFHC Committee has 1000 local chapters and has raised more than $21 million dollars, of which two-thirds finance FFHC projects in 54 underdeveloped countries. The Committee in Madagascar has more than 100 branches and carries on a splendid education program. A national fund-increasing drive in Denmark netted an average of $2 per inhabitant. The French Committee has done a fine job through the schools and with $4 million which it raised it carries on dozens of FFHC projects abroad. The Australian Committee, with around 600 local branches, sponsors an extensive education program at home, and with nearly $3.5 million which it has raised it finances FFHC projects in poorer countries.

The Freedom from Hunger Campaign seeks to mobilize the will of people to *act*, and to learn more about the problem of hunger and malnutrition as they act to do something about it. In this sense, fund-raising campaigns conducted by tens of thousands of children and housewives is instructive equally to the solicitors and givers. But they also serve still another educational purpose because most of the funds go to finance projects in the underdeveloped countries whose main purpose is also educational.

There are hundreds of FFHC field projects in sixty countries of the world, and most of them are executed directly by national FFHC committees or by the private organizations which have raised the money. FAO's advice may or may not have been asked before they were undertaken, and the activity may or may not be reported to FAO. But frequently national committees and governments in the developing countries draw up projects for which there are no donors in sight; and national committees in the richer countries often have funds or potential donors in search of useful projects. FAO therefore acts as a clearing-house. It screens requests for help and maintains a register of approved proposals. It helps find donors for them. And when requested, FAO executes field projects on behalf of donors. By mid-1964 FAO had started more than 50 FFHC projects with about $5 million pledged or paid by national committees and organizations associated with them; hundreds of private direct-action FFHC projects were begun; but FAO had on its register some 135 field requests needing about $30 million for which no donors were in sight.

Most FFHC field projects demand initiative, a great many volunteers, some local funds, and small sums of outside money for technical assistance and equipment. However, some are of considerable size. One of the largest is the fertilizer program which FAO is executing on behalf of the world fertilizer industry in fifteen countries of the Near East, West Africa and Latin America. The program has been going on for three years now and the industry has already contributed $860,000 in cash plus fertilizers. The purpose of the program is to educate tradition-bound peasant farmers in fertilizer use by showing them the effects of fertilizers on their crops. It also aims to train local agricultural extension workers in the techniques of fertilizer demonstration and to determine the most effective and economical fertilizers for local crops and soils. Local administrators participating in the program employ over one hundred full-time extension officers and six hundred part-time field workers. More than 20,000 trials and demonstrations have already been made.

Another large-scale FFHC project is being undertaken by the Swedish FFHC Committee, which has contributed nearly $900,000 to build, staff and maintain a home economics training center in Tanganyika. Still another is a program to install outboard motors on fishing boats around the world. Motors are being furnished by private firms either free or at low cost. For example, the Outboard Marine International has given some 800 engines valued at about $300,000 as part delivery of some 2000 engines promised, and it is also providing maintenance engineers. The Swedish FFHC Committee has allocated $291,000 to provide engines for East Pakistan. And with funds provided by Canadian Churches, the U.K. FFHC Committee, and other sources, fishing boat mechanization is making progress in a number of countries. An FAO naval architect has made surveys in three continents to find out where mechanization can be most profitable.

These projects are impressive, but the big educational job is being done in the large number of small ventures such as that of the Canadian Junior Red Cross, which is financing a program to promote school gardening in Sudan.

While educational field projects have been sprouting, the Freedom from Hunger Campaign has also been moving at other levels. The year 1963 saw especially intense FFHC activity. On 14 March twenty-nine persons gathered in Rome, invited by FAO Director General Sen to a Special Assembly on Man's Right to Freedom from Hunger. All of the guests were persons of recognized international distinction in medicine, science, public service, and industry. Eleven were Nobel laureates. The Assembly issued a Manifesto, calling on the governments and peoples of the world to unite in the struggle against man's common enemy, hunger. "We desire to state with all the emphasis at our command that freedom from hunger is man's first fundamental right."

Later in the month of March the national FFHC committees,

observing Freedom from Hunger Week in nearly seventy countries, carried on coordinated drives to gain publicity, inform and educate, raise money, and start self-help programs. From reports which poured into the office of the FFHC Coordinator at FAO in Rome, the activity was enormous and the impact significant.

A World Food Congress convened in Washington in June 1963, and for two weeks considered the many aspects of poverty and malnutrition. Attended by 1300 prominent scientists and leaders from all over the world, this Congress had been planned from the inception of the Freedom from Hunger Campaign.

In opening the Congress, President John F. Kennedy of the United States called for a concentration of world opinion on the international effort to eliminate hunger as a "primary task of this generation":

> So long as freedom from hunger is only half achieved — so long as two-thirds of the nations of the world have food deficits — no citizen, no nation can afford to feel satisfied or secure. We have the ability, we have the means and we have the capacity to eliminate hunger from the face of the earth. We need only the will. And in the Food and Agriculture Organization, which is sponsoring the Congress, we also have the machinery.

From the Congress emerged conclusions and recommendations, and a declaration "That the persistence of hunger and malnutrition is incompatible with the dignity of human beings and the equality of opportunity to which they are entitled, and is a threat to social and international peace." The Congress recommended an indefinite continuation of the Freedom from Hunger Campaign.

In October 1963 the Third Committee of the U.N. General Assembly, drafting a Covenant on Economic, Social and Cultural Rights, recognized freedom from hunger as a fundamental right. The following month, hundreds of representatives of national FFHC committees and of non-governmental organizations met in Rome, studied FFHC problems, and agreed upon future plans. They also recommended continuation and enlargement of the Campaign beyond 1965, as did the FAO Conference a few days later. In December, on the occasion of the fifteenth anniversary of the U.N.'s Universal Declaration of Human Rights, heads of state or national leaders in more than 100 countries participated in FFHC ceremonies stressing freedom from hunger as "man's first fundamental right".

The most important of all FFHC's achievements has been to lift the eyes of millions above present-day operations to the original aim of the FAO Charter — to free the world from hunger — and to rededicate FAO to that purpose. Another is that FFHC has proved, even though spottily, that private groups, when stimulated and informed by U.N. agencies and encouraged by governments, can be valuable allies in the war on poverty and hunger. Only a start has been made. FFHC Basic Studies have indicated that without a mobilization of private initiatives on a scale far beyond that attained by FFHC, national governments and the U.N. agencies are going to make very slow headway against the backlog of these evils in the world of rapidly growing population.

The U.N. General Assembly in December 1961 declared the 1960's to be a Development Decade and agreed upon a target, to be attained by 1970, of an annual growth rate of at least 5 per cent a year in the national income of each of the poorer countries. Most of the countries concerned, it is now evident, are not going to reach the target at their present pace. With this reality in mind, but encouraged by FAO's Freedom from Hunger Campaign, the U.N. General Assembly in December 1963 directed the Secretary-General to consider organizing a 5-year campaign *against hunger, disease, and ignorance*, to support the Development Decade. The Campaign would involve U.N. agencies and non-governmental organizations in all U.N. member countries. The effect of such a campaign would be either to envelop, or replace, or extend FAO's Freedom from Hunger drive.

While emulation is the sincerest form of flattery, the new proposal raises many difficult questions. The FFHC is aimed not just at hunger but at overall economic and social development, FAO having learned that only in that context can hunger and malnutrition be relieved. Moreover, FFHC specifically covers education and those aspects of health related to malnutrition. Organizing the national FFHC committees has been a long, slow process, chiefly because most governments have not given adequate leadership, and because they and the national committees have failed to provide the FFHC Coordinator at FAO headquarters with enough money to stimulate adequately national activity. According to original plans, the FFHC Coordinator was to have about $750,000 a year, but in fact he has operated on little more than half that amount, all of it provided in the FAO budget. Governments have been reluctant to make special contributions for FFHC headquarters, and the national committees have preferred to spend their money at home or on field projects. Progress in launching FFHC was, therefore, slow. Nevertheless, with time and effort, many obstacles have been overcome and the FFHC is now established and rolling in many countries, with good prospects in many others.

These considerations are apparently taken seriously for the U.N. Economic and Social Council, discussing the matter in August 1964, decided to postpone decision on changing FFHC. But how to enlist hundreds of millions of people in the fight against hunger, poverty, ignorance, and disease is now being studied by the U.N. Secretary-General, the entire U.N. family of organizations, and governments. What will emerge in the way of organization is not certain. But one thing is clear. The need for the help of everybody on earth for the biggest job on earth is gaining recognition. Never again will governments and their creatures, the U.N. agencies, think they can do the job without that help.

FAO is not only continuing FFHC but is planning a new dimension for it. For in spite of all that has been said and done about a war on hunger and malnutrition, there is no plan for conducting the war, and national and regional plans for meeting the needs of growing populations are sketchy. FAO has established the statistics of hunger and malnutrition as the basis for world action and, as we have seen, made important contributions to national and regional planning. But there is still no world plan for meeting the discernible danger of food shortage, much less for abolishing hunger and malnutrition.

The World Food Congress held in Washington in June 1963 pointed this out, and recommended "the holding of the World Food Congress periodically *to review a world survey presented by the*

Director General of FAO, of the world situation in relation to population and overall development, together with a proposed program of future action". This recommendation was endorsed by the FAO Conference in November 1963.

Responding to these cues, Director General Sen has already taken steps to initiate FAO's preparation of an Indicative World Plan for agricultural development. This is an exceedingly difficult and laborious thing to do, but it has been started. As it progresses it will provide an increasingly meaningful framework for U.N. work and also for the Freedom from Hunger Campaign.

The monumental proportions of the task become clearer when it is realized that, to be meaningful, an agricultural development plan must be an integral part of an overall economic development plan covering not only agriculture, but also industry, communications, power, consumption and trade, education, health and the training of skilled manpower. The help of the United Nations and many members of the U.N. family will obviously be needed. The job will take many years. First, FAO must work out a plan for making a plan. The second step is to estimate closely world and regional requirements, at a selected future date, in terms of production, consumption and trade, investment and trained manpower. It is hoped that this can be done in time for review and discussion at a Second World Food Congress in 1967 or 1968. The Indicative World Plan is expected, however, to go beyond establishing requirements, priorities, and targets. These will be merely starting-points for policies and programs to meet the needs.

This is an ambitious undertaking. But with the harsh reality of today's unprecedented, scientifically-induced population flood closing in on the earth's resources, planning the most effective use of those resources is imperative. However, no matter how well man plans the use of the earth's physical resources, no matter how well he carries out those plans, the time will come when he must face up to the fact that population increase must also be planned. For hunger and poverty are not going to be banished from this earth until science is used to control the population flood which it has unleashed. Planned development and population control working together may succeed.

INDEX